LEED® AP BD+C

V4 EXAM

PRACTICE TESTS

(BUILDING DESIGN & CONSTRUCTION)

A. Togay Koralturk

CONTENTS

SECTION 1   INFORMATION ABOUT THE LEED® AP BD+C EXAM   1

     EXAM REGISTRATION PROCESS   1

       HOW TO REGISTER FOR THE EXAM?   1

       WHERE TO TAKE THE EXAM?   2

       EXAM FEES   2

       TESTING CENTER RULES   2

       SPECIAL TESTING ACCOMODATIONS   2

     ABOUT THE EXAM   3

       THE EXAM   3

       EXAM CONTENT   3

       EXAM FORMAT   4

       EXAM TUTORIAL AND EXIT SURVEY   5

       WHAT TO EXPECT AT THE TEST CENTER   5

     AFTER THE EXAM   5

       EXAM RESULTS   5

       PASSING THE EXAM   5

       FAILING THE EXAM   6

       HOW TO MAINTAIN LEED CREDENTIALS   6

SECTION 2   PRACTICE TEST 1   9

SECTION 3   PRACTICE TEST 1 ANSWERS & EXPLANATIONS   39

SECTION 4   PRACTICE TEST 2   69

SECTION 5   PRACTICE TEST 2 ANSWERS & EXPLANATIONS   99

SECTION 6   PRACTICE TEST 3   131

SECTION 7   PRACTICE TEST 3 ANSWERS & EXPLANATIONS   159

APPENDIX A — SUMMARY OF ASHRAE STANDARDS   187

APPENDIX B — IMPORTANT STANDARDS AND PROGRAMS   189

APPENDIX C — PREREQUISITES/CREDITS AND THEIR APPLICABLE RATING SYSTEMS   195

GLOSSARY   199

SECTION 1

INFORMATION ABOUT THE LEED® AP BD+C EXAM

EXAM REGISTRATION PROCESS

HOW TO REGISTER FOR THE EXAM?

1. If you have an existing USGBC site user account, log in to your credentials account to register for the exam at usgbc.org/credentials or create a new account if you don't have one.

2. Make sure that the name you enter exactly matches the name on the ID you will present at the test center. If it does not match, update your name on the website's user account "settings."

3. Review the address in the profile. (The certificate will be mailed to that address.)

4. Select the credential exam you wish to apply for and follow the instructions to complete the application.

5. You will be redirected to prometric.com/gbci to schedule your exam date and location.

6. When the exam is scheduled, you will receive a confirmation number onscreen and an email through Prometric.

    ▪ Print and keep your confirmation number. You will need this confirmation number to confirm, cancel, or reschedule your appointment through Prometric's website, which is prometric.com/gbci.

Once you register and pay for your exam, you have one year to schedule your exam session. You may request one six-month extension of this one-year period.

WHERE TO TAKE THE EXAM?

The exam is administered by Prometric testing centers throughout the world.

EXAM FEES

The exam fee is $250 for USGBC members and $350 for nonmembers.

TESTING CENTER RULES

- At the Prometric testing center, all test takers should present a government-issued photo ID that also contains a signature.
- Nothing can be brought to the exam. Small lockers may be available at the testing center to store your wallet, cell phone, keys, and other small items. However, laptops, briefcases, or large purses shouldn't be taken to the testing center.
- Scrap paper and pencils will be provided by the test site staff and will be collected at the conclusion of the exam. No other paper can be brought into the exam room.
- To leave the room during the exam, test takers should get the test proctor's permission.
- Eating and drinking is not permitted in the exam room.

SPECIAL TESTING ACCOMODATIONS

Accommodations can be requested in case you have a documented disability that would prevent you from taking the exam under normal testing conditions. Prometric complies with the provisions of the Americans with Disabilities Act (ADA).

Any special accommodation should be indicated during exam registration. There is no additional charge for special accommodations.

ABOUT THE EXAM

THE EXAM

The LEED AP BD+C exam contains two core parts. The first core part is the LEED Green Associate exam. The second core part is the LEED AP BD+C exam, which contains 100 randomly delivered multiple-choice questions that should be completed in two hours. LEED Green Associates will only need to take the second core part of the exam in order to earn the LEED AP BD+C credential.

The LEED AP exam can be taken in one sitting. In this case, the exam will take four hours. However, if the test taker passes the first part of the exam, which is the LEED Green Associate exam, and subsequently fails the second part, the test taker cannot earn the LEED Green Associate credential and must then retake the whole exam and pass both parts.

In the exam there will be both scored and unscored questions. Unscored questions are used to collect performance data for USGBC. Test takers will not know if a question will be scored or unscored. As there are both scored and unscored questions on the exam, and the questions are also scaled, there's no way to know how many correct answers you need in order to pass the exam.

In order to pass all the LEED Professional exams, candidates must score 170 points out of 200 possible points. 125 is the minimum score in all the LEED Professional exams. If you are taking the LEED AP exam combined, you should score 170 or higher points on both core parts of the exam. At the end of the exam, you will be able to see your score on screen.

If you have an appeal about the exam content, you can leave comments regarding any question in the exam in case you think there's a technical mistake; however, appeals must be made in the first fourteen days after the test. If your appeal is approved, you will be able to take the test again although your score for the first test will not change.

Make sure you read all the questions and choices very carefully! If a question seems to have more than one answer, make sure you thoroughly understand the question and pay special attention to the wording. It doesn't matter how well you know the exam content, if you don't read the content very carefully, the exam can easily trick you into selecting the wrong answer.

EXAM CONTENT

The LEED AP BD+C exam is intended to test knowledge and skills necessary to support the LEED certification process. The exam evaluates test takers' ability at three cognitive levels:

recall items, application items, and analysis items.

Recall items assess a test taker's ability to recall factual information. Application items assess a test taker's ability to find a solution to a scenario according to the LEED principles and procedures. And analysis items assess a test taker's ability to break down the problem into its components to find a solution by evaluating the relationships of the components.

The exam questions reflect task domains and knowledge domains. Task domains include the tasks necessary to perform LEED effectively, such as team coordination, certification process, analyses required for LEED credits, and more. Knowledge domains include the LEED process, integrative strategies, credit categories, and more.

Below is the breakdown of the exam questions about knowledge domains:

- LEED process
- Integrative strategies
- Location and transportation
- Sustainable sites
- Water efficiency
- Energy and atmosphere
- Materials and resources
- Indoor environmental quality
- Project surroundings and public outreach

The segment about project surroundings and public outreach contains questions about values of sustainable design, regional design, environmental impacts, the necessity of green buildings, and more.

EXAM FORMAT

All the LEED credentialing exams are computer based. Exam questions and answer options will be displayed on screen.

Most of the exam questions are multiple-choice questions that ask to choose the correct answer out of the displayed choices. However, some questions will have more than one answer, in which case the test taker is asked to choose two out of four choices or three out of five. And there will be no partial credit for choosing only one correct answer.

Test takers can leave a question unanswered, flag questions for later review, and change the answer of any test question before the completion of the exam. If you have extra time at the end of your exam, it's highly recommended that you review all the questions.

On the exam, answer every single question since leaving a question blank will not award any points. And if you're unsure about the answer, mark the question and come back to review it later.

During the exam, if you forget something, some later questions or answer choices can make you remember the answer of that previous question.

EXAM TUTORIAL AND EXIT SURVEY

Before the exam, there will be a ten-minute tutorial to demonstrate the exam software. And at the end of the exam, there will be a ten-minute optional exit survey.

During the completion of the tutorial, you can write down any notes on the provided scratch paper that you think will be helpful during the exam.

WHAT TO EXPECT AT THE TEST CENTER

It is recommended that the test takers arrive thirty minutes prior to the scheduled exam appointment. Test takers who arrive later than their scheduled exam time will lose their seat.

Test center staff will escort the test taker to a workstation, and the test taker should remain seated during the exam unless authorized to leave by test center staff. If there is a problem with the computer or you need to take a break, raise your hand to notify the test center staff. However, the exam will not pause if you take a break.

All the test takers should also obey Prometric's security rules while at the test center.

AFTER THE EXAM

EXAM RESULTS

After the exam, your exam score will be displayed on screen, and the test center staff will provide a printed report of your results.

PASSING THE EXAM

As soon as you have passed the exam, you can use the title "LEED° AP BD+C" and/or the logo. As the LEED AP BD+C accreditation will supersede the LEED Green Associate accreditation, the LEED Green Associate title can no longer be used.

Your exam results will be processed within three days, and once the results are processed, a certificate can be requested.

A certificate will be available as a pdf soft copy that can be downloaded at any time for free and as a hard copy that can be requested from the USGBC website for a fee.

FAILING THE EXAM

The full exam fee will be charged for each scheduled exam session after failing an exam.

HOW TO MAINTAIN LEED CREDENTIALS

All the LEED APs with a specialty will need to earn thirty continuing education (CE) hours within two years of earning their credential.

SECTION 2

PRACTICE TEST 1

These practice tests have been prepared in the same format and with the same scope as the actual LEED (Leadership in Energy and Environmental Design) BD+C V4 exam. In these practice tests and in the actual LEED BD+C V4 exam, make sure you read all the questions and choices very carefully. If a question seems to have more than one answer, make sure you thoroughly understand the question and pay special attention to the wording. If still more than one answer choice seems to be the correct answer, choose the answer that best reflects the question. Regardless of how well you know the exam content, if you don't read the content very carefully, the actual LEED BD+C V4 exam can easily trick you into selecting the wrong answer.

 120 minutes

1) A project owner decides not to provide any parking space in the project. The LEED Accredited Professional (LEED AP) tells the owner that the project will earn the Reduced Parking Footprint credit, but will miss another credit with this decision. Which of the following credits will be missed?
   a) Heat Island Reduction credit
   b) Green Vehicles credit
   c) Surrounding Density and Diverse Uses credit
   d) Access to Quality Transit credit

2) Which of the following options under the Daylight credit does not require implementing a computer simulation?
   a) Option 1: Simulation—Spatial Daylight Autonomy and Annual Sunlight
   b) Option 2: Simulation—Illuminance Calculations
   c) Option 3: Measurement
   d) All of the above

3) A new construction project team is pursuing the Option 1: Whole-Building Energy Simulation part of the Minimum Energy Performance prerequisite. If the whole-building energy cost is found to be $20,000, how much energy reduction should be established?
   a) $500
   b) $1,000
   c) $2,000
   d) $5,000

4) A project team pursuing the MR prerequisite, Construction and Demolition Waste Management Planning, couldn't implement reuse and recycling methods and chose to convert the construction waste to energy by following the required European Commission Waste Framework Directive, except for one material stream. What would that one material stream be, assuming that the project would earn the prerequisite?
   a) Metal
   b) Glass
   c) Wood
   d) Aluminum

5) Locating the project under which of the following lighting zones would result in the strictest "uplight" and "light trespass" requirements under the SS credit Light Pollution Reduction?
   a) LZ0
   b) LZ1
   c) LZ2
   d) LZ4

6) Which of the following projects cannot pursue the Option 2: Prescriptive Compliance: ASHRAE 50% Advanced Energy Design Guide part of the Minimum Energy Performance prerequisite?
   a) 80,000-square-foot office project
   b) 90,000-square-foot retail project
   c) 110,000-square-foot office project
   d) 120,000-square-foot school project

7) The project team of a healthcare building project is making a plan to earn the Integrative Project Planning and Design prerequisite. Which of the following is not a requirement under that prerequisite?
   a) Creating a LEED action plan
   b) Preparing the owner's project requirements (OPR) and a health mission statement to be incorporated into the OPR
   c) Conducting a minimum of a four-hour charrette that includes as many of the project professionals as feasible
   d) Developing a "simple box" energy modeling analysis

8) A project team pursuing the LT credit Sensitive Land Protection is thinking about making some minor developments within a wetland. Which of the following minor developments would result in the denial of that credit?
   a) Remediation of the brownfield areas
   b) Activities to restore hydrology
   c) 10-foot (3-meter)-wide bicycle lanes
   d) One single-story structure per 300 linear feet (90 linear meters) on average that does not exceed 500 square feet (45 square meters) to be used as a private office

9) A LEED AP is educating the project team about implementing the integrative process. If the project team also pursues the Integrative Process credit, which of the following credits will this decision make a direct contribution to? (Choose three.)
   a) Optimize Energy Performance
   b) Interior Lighting
   c) Bicycle Facilities
   d) Thermal Comfort
   e) Access to Quality Transit

10) A project team is discussing strategies to pursue the Enhanced Indoor Air Quality credit. A LEED AP suggests Gaussian dispersion analyses. Which of the following would this contribute to?
   a) Carbon dioxide monitoring
   b) Exterior contamination prevention
   c) Interior cross-contamination prevention
   d) Entryway systems

11) Which of the following statements is false about the LEED certification review?
   a) There are only two types of review options for LEED BD+C projects; those options are combined review and split review.
   b) In split review, the design prerequisites/credits are submitted for review during the design phase, and both the additional design prerequisites/credits and all the construction prerequisites/credits are submitted at the end of the construction phase.
   c) In split review, when the design review is complete, GBCI will either mark the design prerequisites/credits as awarded or denied.
   d) An unlimited number of appeals can be made for any LEED project during the LEED certification review.

12) The owner of a residential project is thinking about allowing people to smoke inside their residential units and prohibiting smoking inside all common areas. The LEED AP tells the owner about the additional work that this decision would bring in order to achieve a LEED certification. For this scenario, avoiding which of the following strategies would not result in the denial of a LEED certificate, according to the Environmental Tobacco Smoke Control prerequisite?

   a) All exterior doors and operable windows in the residential units should be weather-stripped to minimize leakage from outdoors.

   b) All doors leading from residential units into common hallways should be weather-stripped.

   c) By sealing penetrations in the walls, ceilings, and floors and by sealing vertical chases, projects should minimize uncontrolled pathways for the transfer of smoke.

   d) Smoke alarms should be installed for the nonsmoking units.

13) Which of the following statements is false about the PBT Source Reduction—Lead, Cadmium, and Copper credit?

   a) This credit addresses lead, cadmium, and copper usage, and it requires projects to limit their persistent bioaccumulative toxic chemicals (PBTs) to the minimums.

   b) It is only applicable to LEED BD+C: Healthcare projects.

   c) For lead, the credit refers to the California AB1953 standard.

   d) Under this credit, projects should not use any interior or exterior paints containing intentionally added mercury.

14) A project located in Barcelona, Spain, is in pursuit of the Option 2: Material Ingredient Optimization part of the Building Product Disclosure and Optimization—Material Ingredients credit. In order to meet the credit requirements, the project team can use products and materials that do not contain substances that meet the following:

   a) Cradle to Cradle criteria for "substances of very high concern"

   b) GreenScreen v1.2 Benchmark criteria for "substances of very high concern"

   c) GreenScreen Assessment criteria for "substances of very high concern"

   d) REACH Optimization criteria for "substances of very high concern"

15) A LEED AP is thinking about addressing the project's emissions with the purchase of carbon offsets to earn the Green Power and Carbon Offsets credit. Which of the following emissions can be addressed by the purchase of carbon offsets?
a) Only scope 1 emissions
b) Only scope 2 emissions
c) Scope 2 and scope 3 emissions
d) Scope 1 or scope 2 emissions

16) For thermal comfort design, which of the following standards is referenced under the EQ credit Thermal Comfort?
a) ASHRAE standard 55-2010
b) ASHRAE standard 55-2004
c) American Council for an Energy-Efficient Economy (ACEEE)
d) ASHRAE 90.1-2010, Appendix B

17) A renovation project pursuing the EA credit, Renewable Energy Production, is estimated to use 100,000 therms of natural gas at a rate of $0.40 per therm as the only energy source. What is the minimum amount of equivalent cost of renewable energy that should be generated on-site in order to earn an exemplary performance point?
a) $4,000
b) $6,000
c) $8,000
d) $12,000

18) A project team is pursuing the Option 2: Renovation of Abandoned or Blighted Building part of the Building Life-Cycle Impact Reduction credit, and it determines that a part of the building should be demolished because of deterioration. Which of the following statements is true regarding the project team's situation?
a) The project team cannot pursue this credit if the deteriorated part is demolished.
b) If there is any deterioration or damage, up to 25% of the building surface area may be excluded from the credit calculation.
c) Unless the deteriorated part is more than 30% of the building surface area, the project team can exclude it from the credit calculation.
d) The project team should not demolish any part of the building; rather, it should continue with the current design.

19) Which of the following project phases is not addressed under the Integrative Process credit?
   a) Predesign
   b) Discovery
   c) Implementation
   d) Operations and maintenance

20) Which of the following statements is false about the Light Pollution Reduction credit?
   a) To earn this credit, any internally illuminated exterior signage should not exceed a luminance of 100 cd/m2 (nits) during nighttime hours and 5,000 cd/m2 (nits) during daytime hours.
   b) The credit addresses all the exterior luminaires inside the project boundary when addressing the credit requirements (except those listed as "exemptions") based on the photometric characteristics of each luminaire when mounted in the same orientation and tilt as in the project design.
   c) Projects need to meet uplight and light trespass requirements by either using the backlight-uplight-glare (BUG) method in option 1 or the calculation method in option 2.
   d) Project teams need to classify the project under a lighting zone, using the lighting zones definitions provided in the Illuminating Engineering Society of North America and International Dark-Sky Association (IES/IDA) Model Lighting Ordinance (MLO) User's Guide.

21) Under the Building Product Disclosure and Optimization—Sourcing of Raw Materials credit, which of the following cannot be considered a biobased material?
   a) Forestry materials
   b) Renewable agricultural materials
   c) Plants
   d) Hide products

22) A project team pursuing the EQ credit Indoor Air Quality Assessment has completed the flush-out. However, per the owner's request, the team has ordered some additional furnishings to be installed in one room after the flush-out. Which of the following actions should the project team take?
   a) There is no need to take any action since the flush-out can occur before installing some furnishings.
   b) The flush-out must be restarted from the beginning for that room.
   c) The flush-out must be restarted from the beginning for the whole project.
   d) Write a credit interpretation ruling and ask for a clarification on this issue.

23) Which of the following prerequisites/credits address showers?
    a) Outdoor Water Use Reduction credit
    b) Bicycle Facilities credit
    c) Indoor Water Use Reduction credit
    d) Outdoor Water Use Reduction prerequisite

24) If a 100,000-square-foot project chooses the Option 1—Path 1: Before Occupancy part of the Indoor Air Quality Assessment credit, how much outdoor air must be provided to the building?
    a) 35,000,000 cubic feet
    b) 350,000,000 cubic feet
    c) 1,400,000,000 cubic feet
    d) 14,000,000,000 cubic feet

25) Which of the following project types should also address "exterior applied products" under the Option 1: Product Category Calculations part of the Low-Emitting Materials credit? (Choose two.)
    a) Schools
    b) Major renovations
    c) Healthcare
    d) Hospitality

26) A project team is searching for refrigeration equipment that can satisfy the requirements of the Option 1: No Refrigerants or Low-Impact Refrigerants part of the EA credit Enhanced Refrigerant Management. Using which of the following refrigerants in the HVAC&R systems would earn the credit?
    a) HCFC-22
    b) CFC-114
    c) Propane
    d) HFC-134a

27) Which of the following project types cannot pursue the EQ credits Thermal Comfort and Interior Lighting?
    a) Major renovations
    b) Core and shell
    c) Retail
    d) Warehouses

28) Under the EA credit, Green Power and Carbon Offsets, projects should engage in a contract that specifies the provision of at least the following:

a) 25% to 50% of the project's energy from green power or renewable energy certificates

b) 50% to 75% of the project's energy from green power, carbon offsets, and/or renewable energy certificates

c) 50% to 75% of the project's energy from carbon offsets and/or renewable energy certificates

d) 50% to 100% of the project's energy from green power, carbon offsets, and/or renewable energy certificates

29) A project team pursuing the EQ credit, Enhanced Indoor Air Quality Strategies is discussing strategies for complying with the "interior cross-contamination" requirements in the printing rooms. Which of the following strategies is an "interior cross-contamination" strategy?

a) Installing permanent entryway systems at least 10 feet (3 meters) long in the primary direction of travel at the regularly used exterior entrances

b) Installing exhaust fans to spaces that may contain hazardous materials or chemicals

c) Each ventilation system that supplies outdoor air to the occupied spaces should contain particle filters or air cleaning devices that have a MERV rating of 13 or higher, in accordance with ASHRAE 52.2-2007

d) Designing the building to minimize and control the entry of pollutants into the building

30) A project team is discussing the number of diverse uses located around a project. A project team member suggests counting a commercial office, which is located within a half mile, as a diverse use. Which of the following statements is true regarding this idea?

a) A commercial office cannot be counted as a diverse use no matter its distance from the project.

b) The commercial office can be counted as a diverse use as long as it includes more than 50 full-time-equivalent jobs.

c) Any commercial office can be counted as a diverse use since it is located within a half mile of the project.

d) The commercial office can be counted as a diverse use as long as it includes 100 or more full-time-equivalent jobs.

31) Under the Enhanced Refrigerant Management credit, retail projects that contain commercial refrigeration systems are subject to additional requirements. However, for newly constructed retail stores, projects with commercial refrigeration systems can provide proof of attainment of _____'s silver-level store certification and automatically satisfy the additional requirements.
a) Cradle to Cradle
b) EPA GreenChill
c) Green-e Climate
d) Green-e Energy

32) Which of the following documents is not required under the LT credit Reduced Parking Footprint?
a) Site plan indicating parking areas and preferred parking spaces
b) Parking capacity reduction calculations
c) Drawings or photographs of signage or pavement markings indicating reserved status of preferred parking areas
d) Signage of the discounted parking rate

33) Which of the following statements is false about the Cooling Tower Water Use Reduction credit?
a) This credit aims to reduce the water usage of cooling towers and evaporative condensers.
b) Projects should conduct a one-time potable water analysis for cooling towers and evaporative condensers to find the actual values of some defined parameters.
c) To gain an additional point, projects can use a minimum of 30% of recycled nonpotable water in their cooling towers.
d) To gain an additional point, projects can increase the cooling tower cycles beyond 10 by increasing the level of treatment in the condenser or makeup water.

34) Which of the following is the type of space that is designed to be used in future expansion and that is typically left unfinished under the MR credit Design for Flexibility?
a) Departmental gross area
b) Shell space
c) Soft space
d) Interstitial space

35) In all three options of the EA prerequisite Minimum Energy Performance, project teams should comply with the mandatory provisions of the following:
   a) ANSI/ASHRAE/IESNA Standard 90.1-2010, with errata
   b) ASHRAE 50% Advanced Energy Design Guide
   c) Advanced Buildings™ Core Performance™ Guide
   d) COMNET Modeling Guidelines and Procedures

36) Locating a project closer to diverse uses can affect which of the following credits?
   a) Access to Quality Transit
   b) Bicycle Facilities
   c) Green Vehicles
   d) Direct Exterior Access

37) Which of following statements is false for Case 1: Demand Response Program Available under the Demand Response credit?
   a) Projects may choose to design a real-time, fully automated demand response system based on external initiation by a DR program provider.
   b) Projects can choose to design a real-time, semiautomated demand response system in which the demand response coordinator initiates the control strategy programmed in the building automation system and the decision to participate is made by a person.
   c) The demand response processes should be included in the commissioning authority's scope of work, including participation in at least one full test of the DR plan.
   d) Projects can design a manual demand response system, which requires the building operator and occupants to manually turn off their end-use systems.

38) A LEED AP of a retail project is working with the project team on conducting a waste stream analysis for the MR prerequisite Storage and Collection of Recyclables to identify the project's top recyclable waste streams. How many waste streams should they identify?
   a) Three
   b) Four
   c) Five
   d) Six

39) "To support the design, construction, and building operations that meet the owner's project requirements for energy, water, durability, and indoor environmental quality" is the intent of the following:
   a) Fundamental Commissioning and Verification prerequisite
   b) Integrative Process credit
   c) Integrative Project Planning and Design prerequisite
   d) Minimum Energy Performance prerequisite

40) Which of the following statements is false about the Places of Respite credit?
   a) The credit is only applicable to healthcare projects.
   b) Projects should provide places of respite for patients and visitors equal to 5% of the net usable program area of the building, and they should provide places of respite for staff equal to 2% of the net usable program area of the building.
   c) A maximum of 30% of the respite area can be located in interior atria, solaria, greenhouses, or conditioned spaces.
   d) Medical care should also be delivered in the places of respite.

41) A project team in pursuit of the Open Space credit wants to calculate the required open space and vegetation area to be provided. If the total project site area is 80,000 square feet, how much open space should be provided, and how much of it should contain vegetation?
   a) 20,000 square feet of open space, and a minimum of 5,000 square feet of that space should contain vegetation
   b) 20,000 square feet of open space, and a minimum of 10,000 square feet of that space should contain vegetation
   c) 24,000 square feet of open space, and a minimum of 6,000 square feet of that space should contain vegetation
   d) 24,000 square feet of open space, and a minimum of 12,000 square feet of that space should contain vegetation

42) Per the Rainwater Management credit, zero-lot-line projects in urban areas with a minimum density of a 1.5 floor-to-area ratio should manage the runoff from the developed site for the following:
   a) The 80th percentile of regional or local rainfall events
   b) The 85th percentile of regional or local rainfall events
   c) The 95th percentile of regional or local rainfall events
   d) The 98th percentile of regional or local rainfall events

43) Which of the following statements is false for the EA prerequisite Minimum Energy Performance?
   a) In this prerequisite, data center projects only have one option and should implement a whole-building energy simulation.
   b) In all the options, project teams should determine the climate zone of the project in accordance with ASHRAE 90.1-2010, Appendix B.
   c) In order to pursue option 3 of this prerequisite, projects should be less than 100,000 square feet (9,290 square meters).
   d) Percentage improvement calculations under Option 1: Whole Building Energy Simulation are based on energy usage.

44) A project team in pursuit of the Site Assessment credit is evaluating the proximity of vulnerable populations that can be affected by the project, adjacent physical activity opportunities, and proximity to major sources of air pollution. Which of the following site assessment categories would this contribute to?
   a) Human use
   b) Human health effects
   c) Hydrology
   d) Topography

45) A project team pursuing the SS credit Light Pollution Reduction wants to modify the project's lighting boundary. Which of the following cannot be considered as an exception to modify the lighting boundary?
   a) If the property line is adjacent to a public area that is a parking lot, walkway, bikeway, or plaza, the lighting boundary can be moved 5 feet (1.5 meters) beyond the property line.
   b) When there are adjacent properties owned by the same entity, and those properties are contiguous to the property that the LEED project is within, the lighting boundary may be expanded to include those properties if they have the same or a higher Model Lighting Ordinance (MLO) lighting zone designation compared with the LEED project.
   c) If there are adjacent properties owned by different entities, and those properties are contiguous to the property that the LEED project is within, the lighting boundary may be expanded to include those properties with their permission if they have the same or a higher MLO lighting zone designation compared with the LEED project.
   d) When a property line is adjacent to a street, alley, or transit corridor, the lighting boundary can be moved to the centerline of the street, alley, or transit corridor.

46) Which of the following systems is required to be commissioned under the Fundamental Commissioning and Verification prerequisite?
   a) Renewable energy systems
   b) Life safety systems
   c) Building envelope
   d) Process equipment

47) Which of the following credits can be pursued without submitting any documentation to GBCI?
   a) Integrative Process
   b) Regional Priority
   c) LEED Accredited Professional
   d) Innovation

48) Which of the following statements is false about the WE prerequisite Outdoor Water Use Reduction?
   a) The baseline landscape water requirement is the amount of water that the landscape of the site will require during the site's peak watering month.
   b) Athletic fields and playgrounds, if vegetated, and food gardens may be included or excluded in the prerequisite calculations at the project team's discretion.
   c) If a project has a landscape that does not need any irrigation beyond a maximum of a four-year establishment period, documenting it will fulfill the prerequisite.
   d) The WaterSense Water Budget Tool of the US Environmental Protection Agency will be used to calculate the landscape water requirement.

49) Under the Minimum Program Requirements (MPRs), every LEED BD+C project must include a minimum of:
   a) 500 square feet (46 square meters) of gross floor area
   b) 1,000 square feet (93 square meters) of gross floor area
   c) 2,000 square feet (186 square meters) of gross floor area
   d) 10,000 square feet (930 square meters) of total site area

50) Which of the following statements is true regarding the LEED Campus program?
   a) It is a streamlined certification process for organizations that plan to certify more than twenty-five prototype-based construction projects within three years.
   b) It is created for projects uniform in design.
   c) It is created for multiple projects that are located on different campuses owned by the same entity.
   d) It is created for multiple projects that are located on a single campus owned by the same entity.

51) How many exemplary performance point(s) is/are awarded under the Innovation credit?
   a) 1 point
   b) 2 points
   c) 3 points
   d) 4 points

52) Under the Option 2: Reduction of Total Waste Material part of the Construction and Demolition Waste Management credit, projects should not generate more than the following:
   a) 1 pound of construction waste per square foot of the building's gross floor area
   b) 2.5 pounds of construction waste per square foot of the project's total site area
   c) 2.5 pounds of construction waste per square foot of the building's gross floor area
   d) 3.5 pounds of construction waste per square foot of the project's total site area

53) Which of the following projects can earn the Option 1: Raw Material Source and Extraction Reporting part of the Building Product Disclosure and Optimization—Sourcing of Raw Materials credit?
   a) A project using 10 permanently installed building materials from 4 different manufacturers with self-declared reports
   b) A project using 25 temporarily installed building materials from 8 different manufacturers with third-party-verified corporate sustainability reports
   c) A project using 20 permanently installed building materials from 6 different manufacturers that are involved in extended producer responsibility
   d) A project using 22 permanently installed building materials from 5 different manufacturers with third-party-verified corporate sustainability reports

54) A LEED Project Administrator is preparing documentation for a pursued pilot credit. Which of the following is not needed?
a) Pilot credit registration
b) Narrative stating that the proposed strategy is significantly better than standard sustainable design practices
c) Pilot credit survey
d) Pilot credit specific submittals

55) According to the Option 2: Multi-Attribute Optimization part of the MR credit Building Product Disclosure and Optimization—Environmental Product Declarations, products that are sourced (extracted, manufactured, purchased) within:
a) 25 miles (40 kilometers) of the project's city will be valued at 200% of their base contributing cost.
b) 50 miles (80 kilometers) of the project's state will be valued at 150% of their base contributing cost.
c) 100 miles (160 kilometers) of the project site will be valued at 150% of their base contributing cost.
d) 100 miles (160 kilometers) of the project site will be valued at 200% of their base contributing cost.

56) How many point(s) are awarded under the Regional Priority credit?
a) 1 point
b) 2 points
c) 4 points
d) 5 points

57) Which of the following products cannot meet the criteria of the Option 2: Leadership Extraction Practices part of the Building Product Disclosure and Optimization—Sourcing of Raw Materials credit?
a) A biobased product that meets the Sustainable Agriculture Network's Sustainable Agriculture Standard
b) A wood product certified by the Forest Stewardship Council
c) A product sourced from a manufacturer with a self-declared report
d) A refurbished product

58) Under the Thermal Comfort credit, all the thermal comfort controls provided should allow occupants to adjust at least one of the four elements in their local environments. Which of the following is not one of them?
a) Air temperature
b) Air speed
c) Surface temperature
d) Humidity

59) According to the Enhanced Commissioning credit, the qualified commissioning authority cannot be a/an:
a) Independent consultant
b) Owner's employee
c) Disinterested subcontractor of the construction team
d) Disinterested subcontractor of the design team

60) Under the Water Metering credit, projects are required to install permanent water meters to some of the following water subsystems that are applicable: irrigation, indoor plumbing fixtures and fittings, domestic hot water, some types of boilers, reclaimed water, and other process water. To at least how many of those subsystems should the projects install water meters?
a) One
b) Two
c) Three
d) Four

61) A project team is in pursuit of the Option 1: Lighting Control part of the Interior Lighting credit. Implementing which of the following strategies would not contribute to that option?
a) Providing multizone control systems that enable occupants to adjust the lighting to meet the group needs and preferences with at least three lighting levels or scenes (on, off, midlevel)
b) Using light sources with a color rendering index (CRI) of 80 or higher
c) Installing switches or manual controls in the same space with the controlled luminaires
d) Making it possible for occupants to separately control lighting for any presentation or projection wall.

62) Which of the following credits is applicable to the LEED BD+C: Core and Shell projects?
   a) Indoor Air Quality Assessment
   b) Interior Lighting
   c) Low-Emitting Materials
   d) Acoustic Performance

63) Implementing which of the following strategies cannot both contribute to the Daylight and Quality Views credits?
   a) Installing vision glazing
   b) Increasing the perimeter floor area of the building
   c) Installing light shelves
   d) Installing low-height partitions or no partitions

64) A project team pursuing the Option 1: Non-Roof and Roof part of the SS credit Heat Island Reduction is discussing design alternatives in order to earn the credit. Which of the following strategies would not make a contribution to the credit's calculations?
   a) Keeping the existing trees at the site
   b) Providing shade with vegetated structures
   c) Replacing invasive plants with grass
   d) Using intensive vegetated roofs

65) A project team pursuing the Option 2: Parking Under Cover part of the Heat Island Reduction credit wants to calculate the number of parking spaces that need to be covered by a roof with a three-year aged SRI of 40. The project contains 100 automobile parking spaces, 10 motorbike parking spaces, and 10 bicycle parking spaces. What is the minimum number of parking spaces that should be placed under cover?
   a) 75
   b) 83
   c) 90
   d) 100

66) Under the Option 2: Reduced Irrigation part of the WE prerequisite Outdoor Water Use Reduction, how much reduction should be established from the project's landscape water consumption?
   a) 10% from the calculated baseline for the site's peak watering month
   b) 30% from the calculated baseline for the site's monthly average water consumption
   c) 30% from the calculated baseline for the site's peak watering month
   d) 50% from the calculated baseline for the site's monthly average water consumption

67) A project team pursuing the Option 1: Historic Building Reuse part of the MR credit Building Life-Cycle Impact Reduction maintains the existing building structure and envelope. However, it removes all the hazardous interior nonstructural elements. The removed portion of the hazardous materials account for 50% of all the interior, nonstructural elements. Which of the following statements best describes the situation, assuming that the building still keeps the "historic" designation?
a) Because the "historic" designation is not revoked, the project will earn the credit under option 1.
b) The project cannot qualify to pursue option 1.
c) The building cannot qualify to pursue option 1. However, it can pursue Option 3: Building and Material Reuse.
d) The building cannot qualify to pursue option 1. However, it can pursue Option 2: Renovation of Abandoned or Blighted Building.

68) Which of the following strategies can qualify for an exemplary performance point under the WE credit Indoor Water Use Reduction?
a) Achieving 55% water use reduction
b) Achieving 75% water use reduction
c) Achieving 80% water use reduction
d) Achieving 85% water use reduction

69) Under the LT credit Access to Quality Transit, what is the maximum walking distance between any functional entry of the building and an existing or planned bus, streetcar, or rideshare stop?
a) Quarter mile (400 meters)
b) Half mile (800 meters)
c) One mile (1,600 meters)
d) Two miles (3,200 meters)

70) A LEED AP is thinking about earning the EA credit Renewable Energy Production without using on-site energy sources. Under that credit, this would be possible with the use of solar gardens or community renewable energy systems if the project implemented the following:
a) Leased the system for a period of at least one year and the system was located within the same district
b) Leased the system for a period of at least five years and the system was located within the same state
c) Leased the system for a period of at least ten years and the system was located within the same utility service area
d) Leased the system for a period of at least ten years and the system was located within the same district

71) A new construction project team is calculating the number of showers that should be provided under the LT credit Bicycle Facilities. What is the minimum threshold for showers that the project team must design for the building?
a) To provide at least two on-site shower rooms with a changing facility for the first 100 regular building occupants and one additional shower for every 150 occupants after the first 100
b) To provide at least one on-site shower room with a changing facility for the first 100 regular building occupants and one additional shower for every 200 occupants after the first 100
c) To provide at least one on-site shower room with a changing facility for the first 100 regular building occupants and one additional shower for every 150 occupants after the first 100
d) To provide at least one on-site shower room with a changing facility for the first 100 regular building occupants and one additional shower for every 100 occupants after the first 100

72) Under the EQ prerequisite Environmental Tobacco Smoke Control, project teams are required to post signage indicating the no-smoking policy. Which of the following statements is true regarding the signage requirements?
a) Signage must be posted within 10 feet (3 meters) of all building entrances.
b) Signage must be posted within 10 feet (3 meters) of the main entrance.
c) Signage must be posted within 25 feet (7.5 meters) of all building entrances.
d) Signage must be posted within 25 feet (7.5 meters) of the main entrance.

73) A project team pursuing the LT credit Bicycle Facilities is working on providing a bicycle maintenance program for employees or bicycle route assistance for employees and customers. What type of project can that be?
   a) Hospitality
   b) Healthcare
   c) Retail
   d) Core and shell

74) Which of the following statements is false about the WE prerequisite Building-Level Water Metering?
   a) Projects should install permanent water meters that can measure the total potable water use for the building and associated grounds.
   b) Metered data should be collected in monthly and annual summaries.
   c) The meter readings can be automated or manual.
   d) Projects should install submetering equipment for major water-consuming systems.

75) A new construction project is pursuing the Option 1: Electric Vehicle Charging part of the Green Vehicles credit. How much electric vehicle supply equipment should be provided in order to earn the credit?
   a) In 1% of all the parking spaces used by the project
   b) In 2% of all the parking spaces used by the project
   c) Equipment capable of refueling a number of vehicles per day equal to at least 2% of the total parking spaces
   d) Equipment capable of refueling a number of vehicles per day equal to at least 5% of the total parking spaces

76) To be eligible for the rating systems under LEED BD+C, at least _____ of the project's gross floor area should be completed by the time of LEED certification, with the exception of LEED BD+C: Core and Shell Development.
   a) 40%
   b) 60%
   c) 90%
   d) 100%

77) A LEED AP of a school project suggests that the school authorities develop and implement a plan through which every bus serving the school would meet the emission standards under the Green Vehicles credit. If the school authorities accepted this suggestion, within how many years should the developed plan achieve this goal?
a) Three years of the building certificate of occupancy
b) Five years of the building certificate of occupancy
c) Seven years of the building certificate of occupancy
d) Ten years of the building certificate of occupancy

78) Which of the following must contain makeup water meters, conductivity controllers, overflow alarms, and efficient drift eliminators under the WE prerequisite Indoor Water Use Reduction?
a) Heat rejection and cooling equipment
b) Cooling towers and evaporative condensers
c) Residential clothes washers
d) Pre-rinse spray valves

79) What is the maximum background noise level that a school project needs to achieve in the classrooms and other core learning spaces under the EQ prerequisite Minimum Acoustic Performance?
a) 20 dBA
b) 40 dBA
c) 60 dBA
d) 80 dBA

80) A 100,000-square-foot mixed-use project, which is being certified under the LEED BD+C: New Construction and Major Renovation rating system, contains both office space (80,000 square feet) and retail space (20,000 square feet). If the retail portion of the building is estimated to have 400 peak visitors, how many short-term bicycle storage spaces will be needed for only the retail portion of the project, according to the LT credit Bicycle Facilities?
a) 6
b) 8
c) 10
d) 12

81) A project team is in pursuit of the EA credit Demand Response. However, a demand response program is not available in the project's location. Which of the following statements is false?
a) The project team should provide infrastructure for future demand response programs or dynamic, real-time pricing programs.
b) The project team should develop a comprehensive plan for shedding at least 10% of estimated peak electricity demand.
c) The local utility should be contacted to discuss participation in future DR programs.
d) The commissioning authority should be excluded from DR processes since a demand response program is not available.

82) Under the Fundamental Commissioning and Verification prerequisite, project teams should prepare and maintain a current facilities requirements and operations and maintenance plan that contains the information necessary to operate the building efficiently. Which of the following is not required to be included in those documents?
a) Construction checklists
b) A schedule for building occupancy
c) Setpoints for all the HVAC equipment
d) A run-time schedule for equipment

83) Which of the following types of spaces cannot qualify to be shared by the public under the SS credit Joint Use of Facilities?
a) Cafeteria
b) Auditorium
c) Health clinic
d) Joint parking

84) How many points can a LEED BD+C project receive by employing two LEED AP O+M principal participants and one LEED AP ID+C principal participant on the project team?
a) 0
b) 1
c) 2
d) 3

85) A warehouse project is in pursuit of the EQ credit Quality Views. Which of the following strategies can result in the denial of that credit?
   a) Achieving a direct line of sight to the outdoors via vision glazing for 90% of the office spaces
   b) Including all the permanent interior obstructions in the credit calculations
   c) Excluding the movable furniture from the credit calculations
   d) For the bulk storage, sorting, and distribution areas, achieving a direct line of sight to the outdoors via vision glazing for 10% of the regularly occupied floor area

86) Which of the following is not a task of the commissioning authority under the EA prerequisite Fundamental Commissioning and Verification?
   a) Reviewing the contractor submittals
   b) Developing and implementing the commissioning plan
   c) Reporting all the findings directly to the owner throughout the whole process
   d) Preparing a final commissioning report

87) Which of the following statements is false about the Minimum Acoustic Performance prerequisite?
   a) It is only applicable to school projects.
   b) School projects should achieve a maximum background noise level of 40 dBA from the HVAC systems in the classrooms and other core learning spaces.
   c) Projects should address HVAC background noise, exterior noise, and reverberation time.
   d) This prerequisite only covers auditoriums, natatoriums, and music performance spaces.

88) Under the Construction Activity Pollution Prevention prerequisite, project teams should create and implement an erosion and sedimentation control (ESC) plan for all construction activities associated with the project. Which of the following should that ESC plan conform to?
   a) 2012 US Environmental Protection Agency Construction General Permit
   b) Phase I Environmental Site Assessment
   c) ASTM E1903-11 standard
   d) American Society of Testing and Materials Environmental Site Assessment

89) A LEED AP suggests that the owner implement daylighting strategies since this will also make a positive contribution to other credits. Which of the following prerequisites/credits would be least affected by this decision?
   a) Minimum Energy Performance
   b) Green Power and Carbon Offsets
   c) Quality Views
   d) Direct Exterior Access

90) The design team is revising the project design in order to minimize the building footprint and to maximize the landscaping. Which of the following statements is false regarding this revision?
   a) This decision will make a positive contribution to the Heat Island Reduction credit.
   b) With this decision, project teams can easily pursue the Open Space credit.
   c) With this decision, the amount of captured rainwater from the roof can be increased, and this would make a positive contribution to the Indoor Water Use Reduction credit.
   d) The Rainwater Management credit would be positively affected by this decision.

91) Which of the following credits considers the individual and multioccupant spaces in addition to the regularly occupied spaces? (Choose two.)
   a) Interior Lighting
   b) Quality Views
   c) Daylight
   d) Thermal Comfort

92) A project team is evaluating the different site alternatives to locate the project. Locating the project under which of the following sites would not result in the award of any points under the LT credit High Priority Site?
   a) A Federal Empowerment Zone site
   b) A brownfield site identified with groundwater contamination where the local authorities require its remediation
   c) State Renewal Zone site
   d) An infill site inside a historic district

93) Under the Light Pollution Reduction credit, which of the following items should the project team consider when addressing the credit requirements?
   a) All the exterior luminaires inside the project boundary without any exceptions
   b) All the exterior luminaires inside the project boundary except those listed as "exemptions" in the credit
   c) All the interior and exterior luminaries except those listed as "exemptions" in the credit
   d) All the lighting elements used by the project

94) In order to meet the requirements of the Site Development—Protect or Restore Habitat credit, a project team is planning to restore the disturbed soils of the site to meet the criteria of reference soils. Which of the following is not a reference soil criterion?
   a) Organic matter
   b) Evapotranspiration rate
   c) Infiltration rates
   d) Soil biological function

95) A LEED AP is making calculations to confirm that the project is eligible to pursue the Path 3: Zero-Lot-Line Projects Only—85th Percentile part of the SS credit Rainwater Management. If the total square feet of the whole lot of the building is 10,000 square feet, at a minimum, how much should the total square feet of the building be in order to be eligible for this path?
   a) 10,000 square feet
   b) 15,000 square feet
   c) 20,000 square feet
   d) 30,000 square feet

96) Which of the following statements is false about the Minimum Indoor Air Quality Performance prerequisite?
   a) Project teams should meet the requirements for both ventilation and monitoring.
   b) Mechanically ventilated projects located outside the United States may choose to meet the minimum outdoor air requirements of Annex B of Comité Européen de Normalisation (CEN) Standard EN 15251-2007.
   c) Projects containing variable air volume systems should monitor the minimum outdoor air intake flow with a direct outdoor airflow measurement device.
   d) The credit refers to ASHRAE Guideline 0-2005.

97) A project team is discussing about alternatives for the pursuit of the SS credit, Open Space. Providing which of the following spaces will not satisfy the credit's requirements?
   a) Pedestrian-oriented paving or turf area with physical site elements that accommodate outdoor social activities for building occupants
   b) Garden space with different vegetation types and species that provide opportunities for year-round visual interest
   c) Garden space dedicated to community gardens or urban food production
   d) Preserved or created habitat that meets the criteria of the Direct Exterior Access credit

98) Which of the following materials cannot be included in the credit calculations of the MR credit Building Product Disclosure and Optimization: Environmental Product Declarations?
   a) Scaffolding with an industry-wide EPD used during the construction
   b) Permanently installed plumbing pipes
   c) Pressurized fire sprinkler piping
   d) Some HVAC ducts

99) Which of the following energy sources is not required to be metered under the EA prerequisite Building-Level Energy Metering?
   a) Biomass converted to electricity to be used for the project by the utility company
   b) Purchased electricity
   c) Energy produced from on-site photovoltaic panels
   d) Natural gas

100) The LEED AP suggests the project team find at least one nonpotable water source and reduce the burden on the municipality-supplied water or wastewater treatment systems. Which of the following would this strategy contribute to?

   a) Outdoor Water Use Reduction credit
   b) Integrative Process credit
   c) Fundamental Commissioning and Verification prerequisite
   d) Cooling Tower Water Use Reduction credit

PRACTICE TEST 1 – ANSWERS

A score above 80 would indicate well preparation for the exam.

1	B		26	C		51	B		76	B
2	C		27	B		52	C		77	C
3	B		28	D		53	D		78	B
4	C		29	B		54	B		79	B
5	A		30	D		55	D		80	C
6	C		31	B		56	C		81	D
7	D		32	D		57	C		82	A
8	D		33	C		58	C		83	C
9	A, B, and D		34	B		59	C		84	A
10	B		35	A		60	B		85	D
11	C		36	B		61	B		86	A
12	D		37	D		62	C		87	D
13	D		38	C		63	C		88	A
14	D		39	A		64	C		89	D
15	D		40	D		65	B		90	C
16	A		41	C		66	C		91	A and D
17	B		42	B		67	A		92	C
18	B		43	D		68	A		93	B
19	D		44	B		69	A		94	B
20	A		45	C		70	C		95	B
21	D		46	A		71	C		96	D
22	B		47	B		72	A		97	D
23	B and C		48	C		73	C		98	A
24	C		49	B		74	D		99	C
25	A and C		50	D		75	B		100	B

SECTION 3

PRACTICE TEST 1 ANSWERS & EXPLANATIONS

1) B
If there isn't any parking area assigned to the project, the project will be awarded the Reduced Parking Footprint credit; however, such a situation would not merit the award of the **Green Vehicles credit** since there is no way to fulfill the credit's requirements without assigning any parking area to the project.

2) C
Under the Daylight credit, option 1 and option 2 require a computer simulation while option 3 does not require any modeling and is created mainly for renovation projects.

3) B
Under the Option 1: Whole-Building Energy Simulation part of the Minimum Energy

Performance prerequisite, projects should demonstrate a percentage improvement in the baseline building performance by implementing a new design. New construction projects should demonstrate a minimum **5%** improvement, major renovation projects should demonstrate a minimum 3% improvement, and core and shell projects should demonstrate a minimum 2% improvement. Since the question refers to a new construction project, the energy reduction calculation would be as follows:

$$\$20,000 \times 0.05 = \mathbf{\$1,000}$$

4) C

Under the Construction and Demolition Waste Management Planning prerequisite, projects that cannot implement reuse and recycling methods can consider waste-to-energy systems if the European Commission Waste Framework Directive 2008/98/EC and Waste Incineration Directive 2000/76/EC are followed. Waste-to-energy facilities must meet the applicable European Committee for Standardization (CEN) EN 303 standards. However, **wood-based products** would be exempt from this additional requirement for incineration and would be directly considered as diversion.

5) A

Under the Light Pollution Reduction credit, there are five lighting zones to classify land use, and there are appropriate lighting requirements that should be met for each. The lighting zones are LZ0, LZ1, LZ2, LZ3, and LZ4. LZ0 is for the areas where the natural environment would be negatively affected by lighting while LZ4 is for areas where high light levels are needed, like Times Square in New York City. So a project located in an LZ0 zone would need to comply with the strictest "uplight" and "light trespass" requirements.

6) C

All project teams can pursue the Option 1: Whole-Building Energy Simulation part of the Minimum Energy Performance prerequisite. However, to pursue option 2 and option 3, projects should meet those options' eligibility requirements.

Option 2: Prescriptive Compliance: ASHRAE 50% Advanced Energy Design Guide is for projects that basically do not contain unique designs and systems beyond simple improvements to the MEP (mechanical, electrical, and plumbing) systems. Office buildings of less than 100,000 square feet (9,290 square meters), retail buildings between 20,000 and 100,000 square feet (1,860–9,290 square meters), school buildings of any size, and hospitals larger than 100,000 square feet (9,290 square meters) are eligible to pursue this option.

In order to pursue the Option 3: Prescriptive Compliance—Advanced Buildings™ Core Performance™ Guide part of this prerequisite, projects should be less than 100,000 square feet

(9,290 square meters), and the project should not be a school, healthcare facility, warehouse, or laboratory.

7) D
Developing a "simple box" energy modeling analysis is a requirement of the Integrative Process credit (not the Integrative Project Planning and Design prerequisite).

8) D
Since a private office is not available to all building users, it would result in the denial of the credit. On the exam, for any question asking for acceptable minor developments under this credit, look first for the answer choice that is not available to all building users. The following are the minor developments that are acceptable within water bodies and wetlands—with the requirement of being available to all building users.

- Brownfield areas can be remediated.
- Grading can be performed to allow for public access.
- Any activity to maintain or restore natural hydrology or native natural communities can be implemented.
- Bicycle and pedestrian pathways can be built; they can be constructed up to 12 feet (3.5 meters) wide, of which no more than 8 feet (2.5 meters) can be impervious.
- One single-story structure per 300 linear feet (90 linear meters) on average can be built, with the structure not exceeding 500 square feet (45 square meters).
- Trees that meet any of the following ratings can be removed:
    - Trees that are under 40% condition rating
    - Trees whose diameters are less than 6 inches (150 millimeters) at breast height
    - Hazardous trees
    - Up to 75% of dead trees
    - Up to 20% of the trees whose diameters are more than 6 inches (150 millimeters) at breast height, with a condition rating of 40% or higher
    The tree conditions mentioned above must be assessed by an arborist certified by the International Society of Arboriculture (ISA), and the ISA measures should be used (or a local equivalent for projects outside the United States).
- Clearings that do not exceed 500 square feet (45 square meters). This is limited to one clearing per 300 linear feet (90 linear meters) on average.

9) A, B, and D
Under the Integrative Process credit, before completing the schematic design, project teams should perform a "simple box" energy modeling analysis and assess at least two strategies

associated with the following: site conditions, massing and orientation, basic envelope attributes, **lighting levels, thermal comfort ranges, plug and process load needs**, and programmatic and operational parameters. In other words, Optimize Energy Performance, Interior Lighting, and Thermal Comfort credits will be positively affected by the pursuit of the Integrative Process credit.

10) B

Under "exterior contamination prevention," project teams should design the building to minimize and control the entry of pollutants into the building. Through computational fluid dynamics modeling, **Gaussian dispersion analyses**, wind tunnel modeling, or tracer gas modeling, project teams should ensure that the outdoor air contaminant concentrations at the outdoor air intakes meet the credit's requirements.

11) C

In split review, the design prerequisites/credits are submitted for review during the design phase, and both the additional design prerequisites/credits and all the construction prerequisites/credits are submitted at the end of the construction phase. When the design review is complete, GBCI will either mark the design prerequisites/credits as **anticipated** (not awarded) or **denied**. No prerequisite/credit will be awarded during the design phase since the design will also need to be implemented on-site during the construction phase. If a design prerequisite/credit is marked as anticipated, it means that the project will earn it at the end of the construction phase once that design is implemented on-site. If it's marked as denied, in order to earn the prerequisite/credit, the project teams will need to come up with a design alternative rather than proceed with that design.

12) D

If smoking will not be prohibited inside the whole building, residential projects should pursue the Option 2: Compartmentalization of Smoking Areas part of the Environmental Tobacco Smoke Control prerequisite. Under this option, projects must prohibit smoking inside all common areas, and this prohibition must be written in the building rental or lease agreements.

Since this option is for residential projects that will allow smoking inside the residential units, each unit must be compartmentalized to prevent excessive leakage between units. Plus, the following would apply:

- All exterior doors and operable windows in the residential units should be weather-stripped to minimize leakage from outdoors.
- All doors leading from residential units into common hallways should be weather-stripped.

- By sealing penetrations in the walls, ceilings, and floors and by sealing vertical chases, uncontrolled pathways for the transfer of smoke should be minimized.
- A maximum leakage of 0.23 cubic feet per minute per square foot at 50 Pa (pascal of pressure) of the enclosure should be demonstrated.

Installing smoke alarms will surely be beneficial for the project. However, this is not required under the Environmental Tobacco Smoke Control prerequisite.

13) D

Projects should not use any interior or exterior paints containing intentionally added <u>cadmium</u> (not mercury). Mercury is addressed by the PBT Source Reduction—Mercury prerequisite and credit.

14) D

Under the Option 2: Material Ingredient Optimization part of the Building Product Disclosure and Optimization—Material Ingredients credit, projects outside the United States can use products and materials that do not contain substances that meet **REACH Optimization criteria for "substances of very high concern."** If the product does not contain any ingredients listed on the REACH Authorization or Candidate list, the product will be valued at 100% of its cost in credit calculations.

15) D

Carbon offsets may be used to mitigate **scope 1** or **scope 2** emissions on a metric ton of carbon dioxide-equivalent basis, and they can be used for both <u>nonelectricity</u> energy sources, such as natural gas, and electricity energy sources.

16) A

On the exam, expect to see some questions with very similar answer choices, as is the case for the question above in choices "a" and "b."

For thermal comfort design, the Thermal Comfort credit refers to the **ASHRAE Standard 55-2010**, Thermal Comfort Conditions for Human Occupancy, with errata or a local equivalent.

The American Council for an Energy-Efficient Economy (ACEEE) defines green vehicles, and it is referred to under the Green Vehicles credit.

ASHRAE 90.1-2010, Appendix B Energy is a standard for buildings, also used to identify a project's climate zone, and it is referred to under the Minimum Energy Performance prerequisite.

17) B

Under the Renewable Energy Production credit, projects should use renewable energy systems to offset building energy costs. The percentage of renewable energy is calculated with the following equation:

$$\text{\% renewable energy generated} = \frac{\text{Equivalent cost of usable energy produced by the renewable energy system}}{\text{Total building annual energy cost}}$$

Since the project is estimated to use 100,000 therms of natural gas at a rate of $0.40 per therm as the only energy source, the total building annual energy cost can be calculated as follows:

Total building annual energy cost = 100,000 x 0.40 = $40,000

And to qualify for exemplary performance under this credit, a project's renewable energy sources should make up 15% of the total energy. (However, only for LEED BD+C: Core and Shell projects, renewable energy sources should make up 10% of the total energy.)

So the project will need to generate electricity with an equivalent cost of the following:

$40,000 x 0.15 = **$6,000**

18) B

Under the Option 2: Renovation of Abandoned or Blighted Building part of the Building Life-Cycle Impact Reduction credit, the building must be renovated to a state of productive occupancy to fulfill this option. **If there is any deterioration or damage, up to 25% of the building surface area may be excluded from the credit calculation.** If the deteriorated or damaged part of the building is more than 25% of the building surface area, project teams should proceed with demolishing those parts and avoid pursuing this option.

19) D

Even though the operations and maintenance phase is a part of the integrative process, it is not addressed under the Integrative Process <u>credit</u>.

20) A

Any internally illuminated exterior signage should not exceed a luminance of **200 cd/m² (nits)** during nighttime hours and **2,000 cd/m² (nits)** during daytime hours.

21) D

Biobased materials are products other than food that are biological products, renewable agricultural materials, or forestry materials. Biobased materials are derived from biomass. Plants and animals can be an example of biobased materials; however, hide products, such as leather and other animal skin material, are <u>excluded</u> in LEED calculations.

22) B

If any partial work occurs during the flush-out in any space (such as installing furnishings), the flush-out process must be restarted from the beginning for that space.

23) B and C

The Outdoor Water Use Reduction prerequisite and credit are related to reducing the landscape water requirement; therefore, they do not address showers.

24) C

During the flush-out under this path, 14,000 cubic feet of outdoor air per square foot of gross floor area should be supplied to the space while maintaining an internal temperature between 60° F and 80° F (15° C–27° C) and relative humidity no higher than 60%.

Total outdoor air to be provided before occupancy:

$$100{,}000 \times 14{,}000 = \textbf{1{,}400{,}000{,}000 cubic feet}$$

25) A and C

26) C

To earn the credit under option 1, projects should either use no refrigerants or only those that have a 0 ozone depletion potential and a global warming potential of less than 50. And propane, which is a natural refrigerant, is the only choice that can satisfy these requirements.

The following table shows the natural refrigerants, and their ODP and GWP values.

Ozone Depletion and Global Warming Potentials of Common Refrigerants			
Refrigerant	ODPr	GWPr	Common building application
Chlorofluorocarbons			
CFC-11	1.0	4,680	Centrifugal chiller
CFC-12	1.0	10,720	Refrigerators, chiller
CFC-114	0.94	9,800	Centrifugal chiller
CFC-500	0.605	7,900	Centrifugal chiller, humidifier
CFC-502	0.221	4,600	Low-temp refrigeration
Hydrochlorofluorocarbon			
HCFC-22	0.04	1,780	Air conditioning, chiller
HCFC-123	0.02	76	CFC-11 replacement
Hydrofluorocarbons			
HFC-23	˜0	12,240	Ultra-low-temperature refrigeration
HFC-134a	˜0	1,320	CFC-12 or HCFC-22 replacement
HFC-245fa	˜0	1,020	Insulation agent, centrifugal chiller
HFC-404A	˜0	3,900	Low-temperature refrigeration
HFC-407C	˜0	1,700	HFC-22 replacement
HFC-410A	˜0	1,890	Air-conditioning
HFC-507A	˜0	3,900	Low-temperature refrigeration
Natural refrigerants			
Carbon dioxide (CO2)	0	1	
Ammonia (NH3)	0	0	
Propane	0	3	

27) B

See Appendix C — Prerequisites/Credits and Their Applicable Rating Systems.

28) D

29) B

For "**interior cross-contamination**," projects should exhaust spaces that may contain hazardous materials or chemicals (in accordance with the exhaust rates determined in the Minimum Indoor Air Quality Performance prerequisite or a minimum of 0.5 cubic feet per minute per square foot of gross floor area), in order to create negative pressure with respect to the adjacent spaces when the doors to the room are closed. These types of spaces should also contain self-closing doors and a deck-to-deck partition or a hard-lid ceiling. Some examples of spaces that may contain hazardous materials or chemicals would be garages, laundry areas, or copying and printing rooms.

Installing permanent entryway systems at least 10 feet (3 meters) long in the primary direction of travel at the regularly used exterior entrances would be an "entryway systems" strategy.

Using particle filters or air cleaning devices that have a MERV rating of 13 or higher, in accordance with ASHRAE 52.2-2007, would be a "filtration" strategy.

Designing the building to minimize and control the entry of pollutants into the building would be an "exterior contamination prevention" strategy.

30) D

Under the "community anchor uses" diverse use category, commercial offices (100 or more full-time-equivalent jobs) can be counted as a diverse use.

Category of diverse use	Use type
Food retail	Supermarket
	Grocery
Community-serving retail	Convenience store
	Farmers market
	Pharmacy
	Hardware store
	Other retail
Services	Bank
	Family entertainment venue (theater)
	Gym, health club, exercise studio
	Laundry, dry cleaner
	Hair care
	Restaurant, cafe, diner
Civic and community facilities	Adult or senior care (licensed)
	Child care (licensed)
	Community or recreation center
	Cultural arts facility (museum, performing arts)
	Education facility (K—12 school, university)
	Education center, vocational school, community college
	Government office that serves public on-site
	Medical clinic or office that treats patients
	Place of worship
	Police or fire station
	Post office
	Public library
	Public park
	Social services center
Community anchor uses	**Commercial office (100 or more full-time equivalent jobs)**

31) B

Under the Enhanced Refrigerant Management credit, retail projects should also meet either option 1 or option 2 for all their HVAC&R (heating, ventilating, air-conditioning and refrigeration) systems. However, stores that contain commercial refrigeration systems must also comply with the following requirements:

- Use only nonozone depleting refrigerants.
- Use equipment with an average HFC refrigerant charge of no more than 1.75 pounds of refrigerant per 1,000 Btu/h total evaporator cooling load.
- Establish a predicted storewide annual refrigerant emissions rate of no more than 15%. Projects should conduct leak testing using the procedures in the EPA GreenChill's best practices guideline for leak tightness at installation.

Alternatively, for newly constructed stores, projects with commercial refrigeration systems can provide proof of attainment of EPA GreenChill's silver-level store certification instead of following the prescriptive criteria listed above.

While Cradle to Cradle certification assesses the ingredients of a product taking into account environmental and human health hazards, it is referred to under the Building Product Disclosure and Optimization (BPDO)—Material Ingredients credit.

Green-e Climate is a carbon offset certification program, and Green-e Energy is a green power certification program.

32) D

Providing discounted parking rates is a requirement of the Green Vehicles credit, not the Reduced Parking Footprint credit.

33) C

To gain an additional point under the Cooling Tower Water Use Reduction credit, projects can use **a minimum of 20% (not 30%)** of recycled nonpotable water in their cooling towers or can instead increase the cooling tower cycles beyond 10 by increasing the level of treatment in the condenser or makeup water.

34) B

Shell space is the type of space that is designed to be used in future expansion and that is typically left unfinished.

Departmental gross area is the area for diagnostics and treatment in clinical departments, and it is calculated from the centerline of the surrounding walls. (Any wall and circulation space within the department is included; inpatient units are excluded.)

Soft space is the type of space whose function can be easily changed. For instance, a management office in a hospital could become a laboratory. Soft spaces should be located adjacent to clinical departments that anticipate future changes and growth.

Interstitial space is an intermediate space between the floors of the building used to run the majority of the building systems (mainly electrical and mechanical).

35) A

In all three options of the Minimum Energy Performance prerequisite, project teams should comply with the mandatory provisions of the **ANSI/ASHRAE/IESNA Standard 90.1-2010, with errata**.

However, only projects pursuing option 2 of the Minimum Energy Performance prerequisite should comply with the ASHRAE 50% Advanced Energy Design Guide. And only projects pursuing option 3 of that prerequisite should comply with the Advanced Buildings™ Core Performance™ Guide.

Under the Minimum Energy Performance prerequisite, project teams may use the COMNET Modeling Guidelines and Procedures for documenting the measures for reducing unregulated loads.

36) B

One of the bicycle network requirements under the Bicycle Facilities credit is to locate the project so that the building's functional entry or bicycle storage is within 200 yards (180 meters) walking distance or bicycling distance from a bicycle network that connects to at least ten diverse uses.

37) D

Under Case 1: Demand Response Program Available under the Demand Response credit, project teams should participate in a demand response program and design a real-time, "fully automated" DR system based on external initiation by a DR program provider.

"Semiautomated" DR—in which the DR coordinator initiates the control strategy programmed in the building automation system and the decision to participate is made by a person—may also be utilized in practice. However, a "**manual**" demand-response system (which basically requires the building operator and occupants to manually turn off their end-use systems) will not satisfy the credit.

In addition, project teams should include the DR processes in the commissioning authority's (CxA's) scope of work, including participation in at least one full test of the DR plan.

38) C

Retail projects should conduct a waste stream analysis and identify a project's top **five** recyclable waste streams (by weight or volume) using consistent metrics throughout.

Once the waste stream study is completed, project teams should list the top four recyclable waste streams and provide dedicated areas for separation, collection, and storage of the recyclables, which should also be accessible to waste haulers and building occupants.

39) A

The following is the intent of the Integrative Process credit: "To support high-performance, cost-effective project outcomes through an early analysis of the interrelationships among systems."

The following is the intent of the Integrative Project Planning and Design prerequisite: "Maximize opportunities for integrated, cost-effective adoption of green design and construction strategies, emphasizing human health as a fundamental evaluative criterion for building design, construction, and operational strategies. Utilize innovative approaches and techniques for green design and construction."

And the following is the intent of the Minimum Energy Performance prerequisite: "To establish the minimum level of energy efficiency for the proposed building and systems to reduce environmental and economic impacts associated with excessive energy use."

40) D

Under the Places of Respite credit, both the dedicated indoor and outdoor areas should meet the following requirements:
- ➥ The dedicated area should be accessible from within the building or located within 200 feet (60 meters) of a building entrance or access point.
- ➥ **No medical care should be delivered in the places of respite.**
- ➥ Options for shade or indirect sunlight should be provided, and projects should install at least one seating space per 200 square feet (18.5 square meters) of each respite area, with one wheelchair space per five seating spaces.
- ➥ Horticulture therapy and other specific clinical or special-use gardens unavailable to all building occupants may not account for more than 50% of the required area.

Universal-access natural trails, which are available to visitors, staff, or patients, cannot account for more than 30% of the required area.

41) C

Under the Open Space credit, projects should provide outdoor space more than or equal to 30% of the total site area, including the building footprint. A minimum of 25% of the provided outdoor space must be vegetated (turf grass does not count as vegetation) or should have overhead vegetated canopy.

With a project site of 80,000 square feet of total site area (including the building footprint), the credit calculations would be as follows:

Required open space: 80,000 x 0.3 = **24,000 square feet**

Required vegetated area: 24,000 x 0.25 = **6,000 square feet**

42) B

43) D

In the Option 1: Whole Building Energy Simulation part of the Minimum Energy Performance prerequisite, the percentage improvement calculations are based on <u>energy costs</u>, not energy usage.

44) B

Under the Site Assessment credit, project teams should prepare and document a site survey or assessment that includes the following categories:

➤ <u>Topography</u>: This covers contour mapping, slope stability risks, and unique topographic features.

➤ <u>Hydrology</u>: This covers flood hazard areas, lakes, delineated wetlands, streams, shorelines, rainwater collection and reuse opportunities, and Urban Hydrology for Small Watersheds Technical Release 55 (TR-55) initial water storage capacity of the site (or local equivalent for projects outside the United States). With TR-55, project teams can model the watersheds to calculate the stormwater runoff volume, peak rate of discharge, and storage volumes. Project teams can also evaluate strategies on rainwater harvesting for irrigation or other uses with this assessment.

➤ <u>Climate</u>: This pertains to the site's solar exposure, heat island effect potential, seasonal sun angles, prevailing winds, monthly precipitation, and temperature ranges.

➤ <u>Vegetation</u>: This covers the site's primary vegetation types, significant tree mapping, threatened or endangered species, unique habitat, greenfield area, and invasive plant species.

➤ <u>Soils</u>: Project teams should determine the soil classification with Natural Resources Conservation Service soils delineation (which is a soil survey showing all the different types of soils), and determine the US Department of Agriculture prime farmland status, healthy soils, disturbed soils, and previous development on-site.

➤ <u>Human use</u>: This includes views, the site's transportation infrastructure, adjacent properties, and construction materials with existing recycle or reuse potential.

➤ **<u>Human health effects</u>: Project teams should evaluate the proximity of vulnerable populations that can be affected by the project, adjacent physical activity opportunities, and proximity to major sources of air pollution.** Additionally, project teams should identify any source of noise, air, or water pollution that can affect the design.

45) C

Under the Light Pollution Reduction credit, projects will need to define their lighting boundary in order to make credit calculations and provide documentation. In LEED, the lighting boundary is located at the property lines of the project. However, there are several exceptions through which projects can modify their lighting boundary, and those exceptions are as follows:

➤ If the property line is adjacent to a public area that is a parking lot, walkway, bikeway, or plaza, the lighting boundary can be moved 5 feet (1.5 meters) beyond the property line.

➤ When there are adjacent properties owned by the same entity, and those properties are contiguous to the property that the LEED project is within, the lighting boundary may be expanded to include those properties if they have the same or a higher MLO lighting zone designation compared with the LEED project.

➤ When a property line is adjacent to a street, alley, or transit corridor, the lighting boundary can be moved to the centerline of the street, alley, or transit corridor.

If there are adjacent properties owned by **different entities**, the lighting boundary cannot be modified.

46) A

Under the Fundamental Commissioning and Verification prerequisite, systems that should be a part of the fundamental commissioning process are:

➤ Mechanical, including HVAC&R (heating, ventilating, air-conditioning and refrigeration)

➤ Plumbing (including domestic hot water systems, pumps, and controls)

➤ Electrical (including service, distribution, lighting, and controls, including daylighting controls)

➤ Renewable energy systems

Systems that are not required to be commissioned under this prerequisite but may be added to the Cx scope at the request of the owner include the following:

- Building envelope
- Life safety systems
- Communications and data systems
- Fire protection and fire alarm systems
- Process equipment

47) B

No documentation is necessary for the **Regional Priority** credit since GBCI will already know the available Regional Priority credits for the project's location, and it will also be able to see if the project team pursued some of them or not.

48) C

Under Option 1: No Irrigation Required, if a project has a landscape that does not need any irrigation beyond a maximum of **a two-year establishment period** (not four), documenting it will fulfill the prerequisite.

49) B

Under the Minimum Program Requirements (MPRs), every project must comply with the following project size requirements under the rating system:

LEED BD+C and LEED O+M rating systems: The project must include a minimum of **1,000 square feet (93 square meters) of gross floor area**.

LEED ID+C rating systems: The project must include a minimum of 250 square feet (22 square meters) of gross floor area.

LEED for Neighborhood Development rating systems: The project should contain at least two habitable buildings and be no larger than 1,500 acres.

LEED for Homes: The project must be defined as a "dwelling unit" by all applicable codes. A dwelling unit should include permanent provisions for living, sleeping, eating, cooking, and sanitation. The LEED for Homes rating system additionally refers to the LEED for Homes Scope and Eligibility Guidelines for extra requirements.

50) D

The LEED Campus Program is not for projects uniform in design, but for **multiple projects that are located on a single campus owned by the same entity**. An example of this would be a university planning to construct several educational buildings on the same campus. These projects can use the LEED Campus Program to pay lower certification fees and streamline the certification process.

On the other hand, the LEED Volume Program is a streamlined certification process for organizations that plan to certify more than twenty-five prototype-based construction projects within three years.

51) B

52) C

53) D

Under the Option 1: Raw Material Source and Extraction Reporting part of the Building Product Disclosure and Optimization—Sourcing of Raw Materials credit, project teams should use at least **20 <u>permanently</u> installed building materials from at least five different manufacturers** that have done the following:

- Publicly released a report from their raw material suppliers that includes raw material extraction locations
- Made a commitment to long-term ecologically responsible land use
- Made a commitment to meeting applicable standards or programs that address responsible sourcing criteria
- Made a commitment to reducing environmental harms created from the extraction/manufacturing process

The following are the valuation criteria for this option:

- Products sourced from manufacturers with self-declared reports are valued at one-half (1/2) of a product in the credit achievement calculations.
- Products with third-party-verified corporate sustainability reports that include environmental impacts of extraction operations and activities related to the manufacturer's product and the product's supply chain are valued as one whole (1) product for credit-achievement calculation.
- Other USGBC approved programs

Materials from the manufacturers that are involved in extended producer responsibility programs can count under the Option 2: Leadership Extraction Practices part of the same credit (not option 1).

And projects meeting the credit's criteria for temporarily used products (such as formwork), cannot meet the credit's requirements since the credit considers only the permanently installed building products.

54) B

A narrative stating that the proposed strategy is significantly better than standard sustainable design practices can be prepared for the Option 1: Innovation part of the Innovation credit, not for a pilot credit. Under the Option 1: Innovation part of the Innovation credit, the proposed strategy should meet the following criteria:

- ➤ Demonstrate a quantitative improvement in environmental performance. In other words, the project should establish a baseline of standard performance and compare the final design performance with the baseline.
- ➤ The strategy of the innovation credit should be comprehensive and should not address a limited portion of the project. In addition, the proposed credit should have at least two components and should not be limited to the use of a particular product or design strategy.
- ➤ **Finally, the proposed strategy should be significantly better than standard sustainable design practices.**

55) D

In order to show compliance with this credit's option 2, the project team needs to calculate the cost of materials in compliance with the option 2 requirements, and it needs to multiply the cost by a valuation factor to show that 50% of all the permanently installed building products have preferred life-cycle impacts.

Let's say that a product meeting the credit's requirements is valued at 100% of its cost according to the credit's requirements. If that product is also sourced (extracted, manufactured, and purchased) within **100 miles (160 kilometers)**—the location valuation factor of LEED—of the **project site**, this time, the product will be valued at **200%** of its cost.

56) C

57) C

Products sourced from manufacturers with self-declared reports will meet the requirements of the Option 1: Raw Material Source and Extraction Reporting part of the Building Product Disclosure and Optimization—Sourcing of Raw Materials credit (not Option 2: Leadership Extraction Practices).

Under Option 2: Leadership Extraction Practices, project teams should use products that meet at least one of the following responsible extraction criteria for at least 25% (by cost) of the total value of permanently installed building products in the project.

- <u>Extended producer responsibility (EPR)</u>: This includes products purchased from a manufacturer that is involved in an extended-producer-responsibility program or is directly responsible for extended producer responsibility.
- <u>Biobased materials</u>: **Biobased products that meet the Sustainable Agriculture Network's Sustainable Agriculture Standard**. Biobased raw materials must be tested using ASTM Test Method D6866 and be legally harvested. Hide products, such as leather and other animal skin material, are excluded.
- <u>Wood products</u>: **Wood products must be certified by the Forest Stewardship Council (FSC) or another USGBC-approved equivalent**.
- <u>Materials reuse</u>: This criterion includes salvaged, **refurbished,** or reused products.
- <u>Recycled content</u>: These products must conform to ISO 14021-1999.
- <u>Any other USGBC-approved program</u>: Any other USGBC-approved program meeting leadership extraction criteria can be used.

58) C

Under the Thermal Comfort credit, all the thermal comfort controls provided should allow occupants to adjust at least one of the following in their local environment: <u>air temperature</u>, <u>radiant temperature</u>, <u>air speed</u>, and <u>humidity</u>.

59) C

In the Enhanced Commissioning credit, the CxA can only be an independent consultant, owner's employee, or disinterested subcontractor of the design team. Note that in the Fundamental Commissioning and Verification prerequisite, the CxA can also be a disinterested subcontractor of the design and construction team, but in this credit, the CxA can only be a disinterested subcontractor of the design team.

60) B

61) B

The color rendering index (CRI) is about lighting quality, and therefore it is addressed under the Option 2: Lighting Quality part of the Interior Lighting credit.

In option 2, the use of light sources with a CRI of 80 or higher for the entire project is one of the eight strategies that project teams can choose to implement in order to earn the credit.

62) C

The LEED BD+C: Core and Shell rating system is for projects in which the developer controls the design and construction of the building core and the mechanical, electrical, plumbing, and fire protection systems. However, it does not involve the design and construction of the tenant fit-out. An example would be an office-building project in which the common spaces are constructed by the developer, and the tenant spaces are left out, allowing the tenants to construct their own custom designs in their office spaces.

Therefore, since the construction will continue in the tenant spaces, the Indoor Air Quality Assessment credit cannot be applicable to these types of projects. Remember that to pursue the mentioned credit, under Option 1: Flush-Out, all interior finishes must be installed, and major volatile organic compound (VOC) punch list items should be completed by the time flush-out is performed. And under Option 2: Air Testing, right after construction and before occupancy, under the ventilation conditions typical for occupancy, project teams should conduct baseline indoor air quality testing by using methods set forth by the USGBC.

Interior Lighting and Acoustic Performance credits are also not applicable because in core and shell construction, the tenants will construct their own custom designs in their office spaces. Therefore, the developer will not be able to force these interior lighting and acoustics requirements on the tenants.

See Appendix C — Prerequisites/Credits and Their Applicable Rating Systems.

63) C

Light shelves are horizontal, light-reflecting overhangs that are positioned to reflect daylight into the desired area of the building. Therefore, they can't provide any views.

64) C

Replacing invasive plants with grass would not make any contribution to the Option 1: Non-Roof and Roof part of the Heat Island Reduction credit's calculations because grass cannot provide any additional shading compared with invasive plants.

65) B

Under the Option 2: Parking Under Cover part of the Heat Island Reduction credit, projects should place at least 75% of parking spaces under cover. Motorcycle spaces are included in the calculations; however, bicycle parking spaces are exempt. So the minimum number of parking spaces that should be placed under cover would be:

$$(100 + 10) \times 0.75 = 82.5—\text{rounded to } \textbf{83}$$

Note that in LEED, this number must be rounded up, not down, even if that value was 82.1

instead of 82.5.

66) C

67) A

Under the Option 1: Historic Building Reuse part of the Building Life-Cycle Impact Reduction credit, project teams should maintain the existing building structure, envelope, and interior nonstructural elements of the historic building or the contributing building inside a historic district. Project teams should not demolish any part of the historic building or the contributing building in a historic district unless it has structural problems or contains hazardous materials.

One thing to note under this option is that this option does not have any threshold for compliance. In other words, the credit does not define any area of the building to be reused or altered. It only requires that the "historic" designation status of the building be still valid after the construction in accordance with the appropriate standards from agencies. If the building's "historic" status was revoked after the historic review, this option could no longer be pursued. (In that case, project teams would be able to pursue Option 3—Building and Material Reuse if they could meet its requirements.)

Also, with regard to this question, since the building would keep the "historic" designation, the project team could earn the credit under Option 1.

68) A

Expect to see a question regarding exemplary performance on the exam. To qualify for exemplary performance under the Indoor Water Use Reduction credit, projects need to achieve **55% water use reduction**.

69) A

Under the Access to Quality Transit credit, the project team should locate any functional entry of the building within a **quarter-mile (400-meter)** walking distance of existing or planned bus, streetcar, or rideshare stops. Or any functional entry of the building must be located within a half-mile (800-meter) walking distance of existing or planned bus rapid transit stops, light or heavy rail stations, commuter rail stations, or commuter ferry terminals.

70) C

Under the Renewable Energy Production credit, the use of <u>solar gardens</u> or <u>community renewable energy systems</u> is also allowed if both of the requirements below are met:

- The project owns the system or has leased the system for a period of **at least 10 years**.
- The system is located within the **same utility service area**.

71) C

All LEED BD+C projects, excluding the residential portion of a building, should provide at least one on-site shower room with a changing facility for the first 100 regular building occupants and one additional shower for every 150 occupants after those first 100. (Also note that in this credit, school projects exclude students, and healthcare projects exclude patients from this calculation.)

72) A

Under the Environmental Tobacco Smoke Control prerequisite, project teams should prohibit smoking inside the building and additionally prohibit smoking outside the building except in designated smoking areas located at least 25 feet (7.5 meters) from all entries, outdoor air intakes, and operable windows. And Signage must be posted within **10 feet (3 meters) of all building entrances** indicating the no-smoking policy.

73) C

Under the Bicycle Facilities credit, unlike the other rating systems, **retail projects** are also required to provide a bicycle maintenance program for employees or bicycle route assistance for employees and customers. An example of a bicycle maintenance program would be to provide coupons for a bicycle tune-up, and an example of bicycle route assistance would be to provide a map that shows bicycle routes to the project site.

74) D

Under the Building-Level Water Metering prerequisite, there is no requirement on installing submeters for major water-consuming systems. However, there is such a requirement under the Water Metering credit.

75) B

Under the Option 1: Electric Vehicle Charging part of the Green Vehicles credit, new construction projects should install electric vehicle supply equipment in **2% of all the parking spaces used by the project**. These parking spaces should be identified and reserved for sole use by plug-in electric vehicles.

Under the Option 2: Liquid, Gas, or Battery Facilities part of the same credit, projects should install liquid or gas alternative fuel fueling facilities or a battery switching station that should be capable of refueling a number of vehicles per day equal to at least 2% of the total parking spaces.

76) B

To be eligible for the rating systems under LEED BD+C, **at least 60%** of the project's gross floor area should be completed by the time of LEED certification, with the exception of LEED BD+C: Core and Shell Development. What is meant by "complete" is that there should be no additional work left for those spaces. For incomplete spaces, projects should submit a letter of commitment declaring that the remaining spaces will satisfy the requirements of the prerequisites and credits achieved by the project, and this declaration will need to be signed by the project owner.

For LEED BD+C: Core and Shell Development projects, the requirement to be eligible for this rating system is to have less than 40% of the interior total gross floor area complete at the time of certification.

77) C

Option 2: Green Buses and School-Owned Vehicles of the Green Vehicles credit requires school projects to develop and implement a plan so that every bus serving the school would meet the emissions standards below **within seven years of the building certificate of occupancy**:

- Nitrogen oxide (NOx) emissions of 0.50 grams or less per brake horsepower-hour
- Particulate matter emissions of 0.01 grams or less per brake horsepower-hour

78) B

The following table shows the requirements for processes under the Indoor Water Use Reduction prerequisite:

Process	Requirement
Heat rejection and cooling	No once-through cooling with potable water for any equipment or appliances that reject heat
Cooling towers and evaporative coolers	Must contain makeup water meters, conductivity controllers, overflow alarms, and efficient drift eliminators

79) B

80) C

One important detail to note for this question is that the project is being certified under the <u>LEED BD+C: New Construction and Major Renovation rating system</u> and not the LEED BD+C: Retail rating system. Projects that are being certified under the LEED BD+C: New

Construction and Major Renovation rating system should provide **short-term bicycle storage** for at least **2.5%** of all peak visitors. On the other hand, the projects that are being certified under the LEED BD+C: Retail rating system should provide **at least two** <u>short-term bicycle storage spaces</u> for every **5,000 square feet** (465 square meters).

However, since the project is being certified under the LEED BD+C: New Construction and Major Renovation rating system, the credit calculations for the retail portion of the project will also be made in accordance with the project's rating system, not LEED BD+C: Retail.

Therefore, the number of short-term bicycle storage spaces to be provided would be as follows:

Short-term bicycle storage: 400 x 0.025 = **10**

81) D

If a demand-response program is not available in the project's location, projects should provide infrastructure for future demand-response programs or dynamic, real-time pricing programs and complete the following activities:

- Install interval recording meters with communications and ability for the building automation system to accept an external price or control signal.
- Develop a comprehensive plan for shedding at least 10% of estimated peak electricity demand.
- **Include (not exclude) the commissioning authority in DR processes, including participation in at least one full DR testing.**
- Contact the local utility to discuss participation in future DR programs.

82) A

Per the Fundamental Commissioning and Verification prerequisite, project teams should prepare and maintain a current facilities requirements and operations and maintenance plan that contains the information necessary to operate the building efficiently. The plan must include the following:

- A schedule for building occupancy
- A run-time schedule for equipment
- A sequence of operations for the building
- Setpoints for all the HVAC equipment
- Building lighting levels
- Any changes in schedules or setpoints for different seasons, days of the week, and times of day
- Minimum requirements for outside air

➥ A preventive maintenance plan for building equipment that is described in the systems

➥ A commissioning program to include periodic commissioning requirements, ongoing commissioning tasks, and continuous tasks for critical facilities

Construction checklists are related to the construction phase.

83) C

Under Option 1: Make Building Space Open to the General Public, with the collaboration of school authorities, project teams should ensure that at least three of the following types of spaces in the school are available to be shared by the general public:

➥ Auditorium

➥ Gymnasium

➥ One or more classrooms

➥ Cafeteria

➥ Playing fields and stadiums

➥ Joint parking

Additionally, in the joint-use areas, access to toilets should be provided after normal school hours.

84) A

The LEED Accredited Professional credit awards only one point for having a LEED Accredited Professional (AP) with a specialty appropriate to the project as one of the principal participants of the project team. In other words, projects can receive only 1 point under this credit even though they employ more than one LEED AP with a specialty appropriate for the project.

However, for this question, the project cannot receive any points, since none of the LEED APs have the LEED AP BD+C credential.

85) D

LEED BD+C: Warehouses and Distribution Centers projects basically have the same view requirements as LEED BD+C: New Construction projects. However, those requirements are only applicable to the office portion of the building.

Additionally, for the bulk storage, sorting, and distribution areas, projects should achieve a direct line of sight to the outdoors via vision glazing for **25%** (not 10%) of the regularly occupied floor area.

86) A

The commissioning authority is required to review the contractor submittals in the Enhanced Commissioning credit, not in the Fundamental Commissioning and Verification prerequisite.

87) D

This prerequisite <u>does not</u> cover auditoriums, natatoriums, music performance spaces, teleconferencing rooms, or special education rooms. It only covers classrooms and core learning spaces.

88) A

The ESC plan created under the Construction Activity Pollution Prevention prerequisite should conform to the **2012 US Environmental Protection Agency Construction General Permit**. The rest of the choices are mentioned under the Environmental Site Assessment prerequisite.

Under the Environmental Site Assessment prerequisite, project teams should conduct a Phase I Environmental Site Assessment in accordance with the ASTM E1527-05 standard, or a local equivalent, and they should determine if any environmental contamination exists on-site. If contamination is suspected, project teams can directly conduct a Phase II Environmental Site Assessment in accordance with the ASTM E1903-11 standard or a local equivalent.

The American Society of Testing and Materials (ASTM) Environmental Site Assessment is the methodology used in LEED to investigate a project site's contamination.

89) D

Increasing daylighting will affect the building's energy use and will therefore affect the Minimum Energy Performance prerequisite and the Green Power and Carbon Offsets credit.

Implementing daylighting strategies will also make a big contribution to the Quality Views credit since most strategies used for daylighting are also used to provide views.

However, the Direct Exterior Access credit will not be affected by this decision since this credit addresses exterior spaces rather than daylighting, views, or energy.

90) C

By minimizing the building footprint, the roof area will also be minimized. Therefore, the amount of captured rainwater from the roof would actually decrease.

However, increasing the landscaping would for sure make a great contribution to the Heat Island Reduction and Rainwater Management credits since it would decrease the area of impermeable surfaces while increasing the area of permeable surfaces.

Open space credit would also be positively affected by this decision (if the rest of the credit's requirements were also met) since the amount of open space would also be increased.

91) A and D

Quality Views and Daylight credits consider the regularly occupied spaces, not the individual or the multioccupant spaces.

92) C

Under Option 2: Priority Designation, the project site must be located in one of the following priority development areas:

- A site listed by the EPA National Priorities List
- A Federal Empowerment Zone site
- A Federal Enterprise Community site
- A Federal (not state) Renewal Community site
- A site within a Department of the Treasury Community Development Financial Institutions Fund Qualified Low-Income Community (a subset of the New Markets Tax Credit Program)
- A site in a US Department of Housing and Urban Development's Qualified Census Tract (QCT) or Difficult Development Area (DDA)
- For projects outside the United States, sites that meet the same types of specifications of a local equivalent program administered at the national level

A site inside the **State Renewal Zone** is not mentioned in the credit.

93) B

Under the Light Pollution Reduction credit, project teams should consider <u>all the exterior luminaires inside the project boundary when addressing the credit requirements (except those listed as "exemptions")</u> based on the following:

- The photometric characteristics of each luminaire when mounted in the same orientation and tilt as in the project design.
- The lighting zone of the project property at the time construction starts.

Below are the types of lighting that are exempt from the credit requirements if they are controlled separately from the nonexempt lighting:

- Specialized signal, directional, and marker lighting for transportation
- Lighting solely used for facade and landscape lighting in MLO lighting zones 3 and 4 and that is automatically turned off from midnight to 6:00 a.m.
- Government-mandated roadway lighting
- Lighting for theatrical purposes, stages, and video performances
- Hospital emergency department and helipad lighting
- National flag lighting in MLO lighting zones 2, 3, or 4
- Internally illuminated signage (this has its own requirement in the following pages)

Interior luminaires are not addressed under this credit.

94) B

In order to meet the requirements of the Site Development—Protect or Restore Habitat credit, the restored soil should meet the criteria of reference soils (reference soils are the native soils of a site that were present before the development) in categories 1, 2, and 3 and meet the criteria of either category 4 or 5:

1. Organic matter
2. Compaction
3. Infiltration rates
4. Soil biological function
5. Soil chemical characteristics

Evapotranspiration is the term used for the return of water to the atmosphere through evaporation from plants.

95) B

Path 3 of the Rainwater Management credit is only for zero-lot-line projects in urban areas with a minimum density of a **1.5 floor-to-area ratio**. (Zero-lot-line projects are types of projects in which the buildings are built on the entire lot.)

The floor-to-area ratio is also a very important term for the exam, and it is calculated by dividing the total square feet of a building by the total square feet of the lot of the building. For example, 10,000 square feet of land that has a FAR of 2 would allow the construction of a 20,000-square-foot building. If the building had two stories, each story could contain 10,000 square feet of space. In this case, the building would cover the whole lot since the lot also measures 10,000 square feet.

For this question, since the project should have a minimum density of a 1.5 floor-to-area ratio, the total square feet of the building should be 15,000 square feet at a minimum.

$$1.5 \text{ FAR} = \textbf{15,000 square feet} / 10,000\text{square feet}$$

96) D

LEED refers to ASHRAE Guideline 0-2005 under the Fundamental Commissioning and Verification prerequisite and the Enhanced Commissioning credit.

97) D

Under the Open Space credit, the outdoor space must be physically accessible and be one or more of the following:

- A pedestrian-oriented paving or turf area with physical site elements that accommodate outdoor social activities for building occupants

◆ A recreation-oriented paving or turf area with physical site elements to encourage physical activity for building occupants

◆ A garden space with different vegetation types and species that provide opportunities for year-round visual interest

◆ A garden space dedicated to community gardens or urban food production

◆ **A preserved or created habitat that meets the criteria of the Site Development— Protect or Restore Habitat credit** (not the Direct Exterior Access credit) and also includes elements of human interaction

98) A

Under the BPDO: Environmental Product Declarations credit, all the qualifying products must be permanently installed products for both options 1 and 2. For LEED, mechanical, electrical, plumbing, and furniture items are not considered permanently installed building products and are typically excluded from the credit calculations. However, if the project team considers them "permanently installed building products," they can be included in the credit calculations as long as they are also included in the other BPDO credits, which are BPDO: Environmental Product Declarations and BPDO: Material Ingredients.

In other words, all choices except the scaffolding can be included in the credit calculations as long as they are also included in the other BPDO credits.

However, scaffolding used during construction cannot be considered a permanently installed product and therefore must be excluded from the credit calculations.

99) C

Under the Building-Level Energy Metering prerequisite, projects should install new building-level energy meters/submeters, or use existing ones, that can be aggregated to provide a measurement of total building energy consumption, including electricity, natural gas, chilled water, steam, fuel oil, propane and biomass energy sources. However, the prerequisite does not require metering of the locally generated sources dedicated to the project, such as **photovoltaic panels** or wind-generated electricity.

100) B

Under the Integrative Process credit, a project team should evaluate all of the following: indoor water demand, outdoor water demand, process water demand, and supply sources. Next, the credit requires that a project find **at least one nonpotable water source and reduce the burden on the municipality-supplied water or wastewater treatment systems** by contributing to at least two of the water demand components listed above.

SECTION 4

PRACTICE TEST 2

These practice tests have been prepared in the same format and with the same scope as the actual LEED BD+C V4 exam. In these practice tests and in the actual LEED BD+C V4 exam, make sure you read all the questions and choices very carefully. If a question seems to have more than one answer, make sure you thoroughly understand the question and pay special attention to the wording. If still more than one answer choice seems to be the correct answer, choose the answer that best reflects the question. Regardless of how well you know the exam content, if you don't read the content very carefully, the actual LEED BD+C V4 exam can easily trick you into selecting the wrong answer.

 120 minutes

1) A LEED AP is making calculations to figure out the number of parking spaces that should be placed under cover per the Option 2: Parking Under Cover part of the Heat Island Reduction credit. What percent of the parking spaces should be placed under cover?
   a) 50% of the total parking spaces (motorcycle spaces are included in the calculations; however, bicycle parking spaces are exempt)
   b) 75% of the total parking spaces (motorcycle spaces and bicycle parking spaces are included in the calculations)
   c) 75% of the total parking spaces (motorcycle spaces are included in the calculations; however, bicycle parking spaces are exempt)
   d) 100% of the total parking spaces

2) A project team is working on fulfilling the energy-related requirements of the Integrative Process credit. The project team is evaluating multifunctioning spaces, space allotment per person, operating schedules, and anticipated operations and maintenance. Which of the following will this contribute to?
   a) Basic envelope attributes
   b) Plug and process load needs
   c) Programmatic and operational parameters
   d) Massing and orientation

3) A project team pursuing the EA credit Green Power and Carbon Offsets is going to make a contract with a renewable energy certificate provider in order to earn the credit. At a minimum, how long should the contract be?
   a) 1 year
   b) 2 years
   c) 5 years
   d) 10 years

4) In some EQ prerequisites/credits, the "spaces" inside the building are categorized as "occupied spaces," or as "unoccupied spaces." Which of the following space types cannot be categorized as unoccupied spaces?
   a) Corridors
   b) Emergency exit corridors
   c) Mechanical rooms
   d) Electrical rooms

5) In order to earn the Sensitive Land Protection credit under option 2, the development footprint or a portion of it can be located as follows:
   a) Inside prime farmland as defined by the US Department of Agriculture, United States Code of Federal Regulations Title 7, Volume 6, Parts 400 to 699, Section 657.5 and identified in a state Natural Resources Conservation Service (NCRS) soil survey
   b) Within 60 feet (18 meters) of a wetland
   c) İnside a habitat that contains species listed as threatened or endangered under the US Endangered Species Act or the state's endangered species act
   d) Inside a flood hazard area shown on a legally adopted flood hazard map by the Federal Emergency Management Agency

6) Pursuing which of the following prerequisites/credits may require conducting an environmental site assessment (ESA)? (Choose two.)
   a) Environmental Site Assessment prerequisite
   b) High-Priority Site credit
   c) Open Space credit
   d) Integrative Process credit

7) In order to earn the maximum number of points from the Enhanced Commissioning credit, which of the following paths/options should be pursued?
   a) Option 1: Path 2—Enhanced and Monitoring-Based Commissioning and Option 2: Envelope Commissioning
   b) Option 1: Path 1—Enhanced Commissioning and Option 1: Path 2—Enhanced and Monitoring-Based Commissioning
   c) Only Option 2: Envelope Commissioning
   d) Option 1: Path 1—Enhanced Commissioning and Option 2: Envelope Commissioning

8) Which of the following statements is false regarding the Quality Views credit?
   a) In the credit calculations, project teams should include all the permanent interior obstructions while the movable furniture and partitions can be excluded.
   b) Views into interior atria can be used to meet up to 30% of the required quality view area.
   c) For the bulk storage, sorting, and distribution areas, LEED BD+C: Warehouses and Distribution Centers should meet the view requirements for only 50% of the regularly occupied floor area.
   d) A LEED BD+C: Healthcare project can earn an extra point by meeting the perimeter floor-area requirements.

9) According to LEED, for a piece of land to be qualified as an "infill site," at least _____ of the land should be already developed within a half mile (800 meters) of the project boundary.
   a) 25%
   b) 50%
   c) 75%
   d) 100%

10) Which of the following strategies of the Enhanced Indoor Air Quality credit does not address the Chartered Institution of Building Services Engineers (CIBSE) applications manual?
   a) Mixed-mode design calculations
   b) Natural ventilation design calculations
   c) Additional source control and monitoring
   d) Natural ventilation room-by-room calculations

11) In which of the following LEED certification phases does the LEED Project Administrator need to be assigned?
   a) Registration
   b) Application
   c) Review
   d) Certification or denial

12) Per the Environmental Tobacco Smoke Control prerequisite, project teams should prohibit smoking inside the building and additionally prohibit smoking outside the building except in designated smoking areas located at least _____.
   a) 16 feet (5 meters) from all entries and operable windows
   b) 25 feet (7.5 meters) from all entries, outdoor air intakes, and operable windows
   c) 50 feet (15 meters) from all entries, outdoor air intakes, and operable windows
   d) 50 feet (22.5 meters) from all entries

13) Which of the following credits refers to the GreenScreen v1.2 Benchmark?
   a) Building Product Disclosure and Optimization—Sourcing of Raw Materials
   b) Building Product Disclosure and Optimization—Material Ingredients
   c) PBT Source Reduction—Mercury
   d) Building Product Disclosure and Optimization—Environmental Product Declarations

14) The LEED Volume Program is a streamlined certification process for organizations that plan to certify the following:
   a) More than twenty prototype-based projects within three years
   b) More than twenty projects owned by the same entity, not uniform in design
   c) More than twenty-five prototype-based projects within three years
   d) Multiple projects that are located on a single campus owned by the same entity

15) Which of the following statements is false about the Furniture and Medical Furnishings credit?
   a) It is only applicable to LEED BD+C: Healthcare projects.
   b) Under the credit, at least 30% (1 point) or 40% (2 points), by cost, of all the freestanding furniture and medical furnishings should meet the credit's criteria in one of the three options.
   c) Any new furniture or medical furnishing assemblies must be in accordance with ANSI/BIFMA Standard Method M7.1-2011.
   d) All the medical furnishings used in the project should contain environmental product declarations.

16) Per the MR prerequisite Construction and Demolition Waste Management Planning, projects should develop and implement a construction and demolition waste management plan and establish waste diversion goals by identifying at least:
   a) Four materials (nonstructural) targeted for diversion
   b) Four materials (both structural and nonstructural) targeted for diversion
   c) Five materials (both structural and nonstructural) targeted for diversion
   d) Six materials (structural) targeted for diversion

17) With the MR prerequisite Storage and Collection of Recyclables, all projects except retail should take the necessary actions for safe collection, storage, and disposal of two of the following three items: (Choose three.)
   a) Batteries
   b) Electronic waste
   c) Mercury-containing lamps
   d) Lead-containing lamps
   e) Electronic waste containing persistent bioaccumulative and toxic chemicals (PBTs)

18) Locating a LEED BD+C: Retail project under which of the following sites would result in the achievement of the LT credit LEED for Neighborhood Development Location?
    a) LEED ND Pilot—Stage 1 LEED for Neighborhood Development Prereviewed Plan
    b) LEED 2009—Stage 1 Conditional Approval of LEED ND Plan
    c) LEED v4—LEED for Neighborhood Development Conditional Approval
    d) LEED 2009—Stage 2 Precertified LEED for Neighborhood Development Plan

19) Per the Green Power and Carbon Offsets credit, all the purchased carbon offsets should be:
    a) Green-e Energy-certified or equivalent
    b) Green-e Climate-certified or equivalent
    c) EPA GreenChill-certified or equivalent
    d) Cradle to Cradle-certified or equivalent

20) Which of the following statements is false regarding the Option 1: Historic Building Reuse part of the Building Life-Cycle Impact Reduction credit?
    a) Project teams should not demolish any part of the historic building or the contributing building in a historic district unless it has structural problems or contains hazardous materials.
    b) Any alteration, such as preservation, restoration, or rehabilitation, must be conducted in accordance with the local or national standards for rehabilitation, wherever applicable.
    c) Under this option, the "historic" designation status of the building is not required to be valid after completion of construction.
    d) If the building is not subject to historic review, a preservation professional who meets the United States' federal qualifications for historic architects should be included in the project team.

21) Which of the following energy sources cannot qualify under the EA credit Renewable Energy Production?
    a) Tidal
    b) Wave
    c) Passive solar
    d) Geothermal energy

22) Using which of the following glare control devices can satisfy the requirements of the Daylight credit?
   a) Fixed exterior overhangs
   b) Operable window blinds
   c) Fixed fins
   d) Frit glazing treatment

23) A school project is pursuing the Option 2: Green Buses and School-Owned Vehicles part of the Green Vehicles credit. The project team is discussing retrofitting some of the buses in order to meet the emission standards of the credit. Which of the following third parties should approve the retrofitting?
   a) American Council for an Energy-Efficient Economy (ACEEE)
   b) Green-e
   c) California Air Resources Board
   d) SMACNA

24) Which of the following credits requires project teams to regularly document site photographs?
   a) Enhanced Indoor Air Quality Strategies credit
   b) Construction Indoor Air Quality Management Plan credit
   c) Open Space credit
   d) Indoor Air Quality Assessment credit

25) Before the start of the project design, a LEED AP suggests that the owner implement green building strategies and aim for a LEED certification. Which of the following statements is false about developing green buildings?
   a) Many municipalities award structural incentives to green buildings such as reducing the review and permitting durations in exchange for developers' establishment of green building standards.
   b) Many municipalities allow for percentage increases in floor-to-area ratio or other measures of density contingent upon certification or proof of green building practices.
   c) Some municipalities offer reductions or waivers for permit review or other less onerous permitting processes in exchange for developers' use of green building standards.
   d) If a developer is unfamiliar with green building practices, it is better not to design for a green building.

26) Under the Low-Emitting Materials credit, which of the following is the emission and content requirement for "flooring"?
   a) General emissions evaluation
   b) Composite wood evaluation
   c) VOC content requirement for wet-applied products
   d) Additional insulation requirements

27) A project team determines that some of the materials (mostly furniture) that have been installed in the project cannot meet the requirements of the Option 1: Product Category Calculations part of the Low-Emitting Materials credit. Which of the following strategies should a LEED AP suggest?
   a) Pursue Option 2: Budget Calculation Method and show that the overall VOC level in the building is less than the maximum threshold by calculating the weighted averages of each material's VOC level
   b) Pursue another credit instead of the Low-Emitting Materials credit
   c) Exclude furniture from the credit calculations since furniture can be excluded at the project team's discretion
   d) Pursue Option 2: Budget Calculation Method and omit furniture from the credit calculations

28) The Environmental Site Assessment prerequisite is applicable to which of the following rating systems?
   a) Only to LEED BD+C: Schools
   b) Only to LEED BD+C: Healthcare
   c) Only to LEED BD+C: Schools and LEED BD+C: Healthcare
   d) All the LEED BD+C rating systems

29) Which of the following enables international projects to earn prerequisites/credits by allowing them to meet international standards or their local standards instead of US-based standards?
   a) Alternative compliance paths (ACPs)
   b) Credit Interpretation Rulings (CIR)
   c) Addenda
   d) Alternative credits

30) Which of the following refrigerants contains the least ozone depletion potential (ODP)?
   a) Hydrofluorocarbon-410A
   b) Chlorofluorocarbon-11
   c) Chlorofluorocarbon-114
   d) Hydrochlorofluorocarbon-22

31) "To assess site conditions prior to design in order to evaluate sustainable options and inform related decisions about site design" is the intent of which of the following?
   a) Site Assessment credit
   b) Fundamental Commissioning and Verification prerequisite
   c) Enhanced Commissioning and Verification credit
   d) Integrative Project Planning and Design prerequisite

32) Under the Fundamental Refrigerant Management prerequisite, when reusing existing HVAC&R equipment, project teams should complete a comprehensive CFC phase-out conversion before _____.
   a) The LEED certification date
   b) Typical occupancy
   c) Project completion
   d) The construction permit issue date

33) Under the Option 2: Renovation of Abandoned or Blighted Building part of the Building Life-Cycle Impact Reduction credit, projects should maintain at least _____, by surface area, of the existing building structure, enclosure, and interior structural elements for buildings that meet local criteria of abandoned buildings or are considered blighted.
   a) 30%
   b) 40%
   c) 50%
   d) 60%

34) LEED AP suggests reducing the pavement area in order to increase the vegetated area. Which of the following credits will be least affected by this decision?
   a) Heat Island Reduction
   b) Outdoor Water Use Reduction
   c) Reduced Parking Footprint
   d) Rainwater Management

35) Which of the following statements is false about the Reduced Parking Footprint credit?
   a) Base parking ratios are referenced by the Parking Consultants Council, as shown in the Institute of Transportation Engineers' Transportation Planning Handbook, 3rd edition, tables 18-2 through 18-4.
   b) Projects need to provide preferred parking for carpools for 10% of the total parking after the reductions have been made from the base ratios.
   c) Projects without off-street parking will earn the credit automatically.
   d) Projects that have earned 1 or more points under either the Surrounding Density and Diverse Uses credit or the Access to Quality Transit credit should achieve a 40% reduction from the base ratios.

36) In order to earn the maximum points (neglecting exemplary performance) under the EA credit Renewable Energy Production, new construction projects should use renewable energy systems that account for the following:
   a) 5% of the total building annual energy cost
   b) 10% of the total building annual energy cost
   c) 15% of the total building annual energy cost
   d) 20% of the total building annual energy cost

37) Which of the following project types are required to consider the "perimeter floor area" instead of the "regularly occupied floor area" under the Daylight credit calculations?
   a) Retail
   b) Core and shell
   c) Healthcare
   d) Major renovation

38) How many prerequisites does the Location and Transportation category contain?
   a) 0
   b) 1
   c) 2
   d) 3

39) The project owner is thinking about using an existing refrigerant unit that contains 3 pounds (1,350 grams) of refrigerant. The LEED AP tells the owner that this will result in the denial of a LEED certificate. How much refrigerant should the existing equipment contain in order not to lose the LEED certification?
a) 0.5 pound (225 grams)
b) 0.75 pound (340 grams)
c) 1 pound (450 grams)
d) 2 pounds (900 grams)

40) Which of the following statements about diverse use calculations is false for the LT credit Surrounding Density and Diverse Uses?
a) If there are "four" supermarkets within walking distance of the building's main entrance, they can only be counted as "two" diverse uses.
b) A retail store that contains a pharmacy and a supermarket under the same store can be counted as "two" diverse uses.
c) The counted diverse uses must be present under at least three of the five diverse use categories.
d) Planned but currently not operating diverse uses can be counted if the diverse use will be active within one year of the date that the project accepts the initial certificate of occupancy.

41) Which of the following standards is related to air filters?
a) ASHRAE standard 52.2-2007
b) ASHRAE standard 55-2010
c) ASHRAE standard 170-2008
d) CIBSE Applications Manual AM10

42) Under the Advanced Energy Metering credit, project teams should install advanced energy metering for any individual energy end uses that consume _____ or more of the total annual consumption of the building.
a) 5%
b) 8%
c) 10%
d) 15%

43) A LEED AP determines that a demand-response program is available in the project's location. In order to pursue the EA credit Demand Response, how long at a minimum should the project enroll in the program with the intention of multiyear renewal?
   a) One year
   b) Two years
   c) Five years
   d) Ten years

44) ANSI/BIFMA Standard Method M7.1-2011 is addressed under the EQ credit Low-Emitting Materials for the following:
   a) Additional insulation requirements
   b) Exterior applied products
   c) Furniture evaluation
   d) Composite wood evaluation

45) Which of the following statements is false about the EA credit Enhanced Commissioning?
   a) In addition to implementing an enhanced systems commissioning, projects can also choose to implement monitor-based commissioning (MBCx) to gain an additional point under Option 1: Enhanced Systems Commissioning.
   b) In the credit's Option 1: Path 1—Enhanced Commissioning, project teams will need to implement enhanced systems commissioning.
   c) When pursuing this credit, the additional commissioning requirements should also be included in the OPR, the BOD, and the Cx plan.
   d) The credit refers to the ANSI/ASHRAE/IESNA Standard 90.1.-2010, Appendix G, with errata.

46) Which of the following approaches is used for conducting a life-cycle analysis under the Option 4: Whole-Building Life-Cycle Assessment part of the Building Life-Cycle Impact Reduction credit?
   a) Cradle to gate
   b) Cradle to grave
   c) Cradle to cradle
   d) REACH Optimization

47) Which of the following is the type of space where people spend time totaling more than one hour of continuous occupancy per person per day on average?
   a) Regularly occupied spaces
   b) Nonregularly occupied spaces
   c) Individual occupant spaces
   d) Occupied space

48) Which of the following project types is eligible to pursue the Option 3: Prescriptive Compliance—Advanced Buildings™ Core Performance™ Guide part of the Minimum Energy Performance prerequisite?
   a) Warehouse
   b) School
   c) Office
   d) Healthcare

49) A LEED AP is aiming for the maximum number of points under the Optimize Energy Performance credit. Which of the following options should be pursued under the Minimum Energy Performance prerequisite?
   a) Option 1: Whole-Building Energy Simulation
   b) Option 2: Prescriptive Compliance: ASHRAE Advanced Energy Design Guide
   c) Option 3: Prescriptive Compliance: Advanced Buildings™ Core Performance™ Guide
   d) Both Option 1: Whole-Building Energy Simulation and Option 2: Prescriptive Compliance: ASHRAE Advanced Energy Design Guide

50) Which of the following statements is false about the SS credit Direct Exterior Access?
   a) Under the credit, projects should provide direct access to an exterior courtyard, terrace, garden, or balcony.
   b) The provided space must be at least 5 square feet (0.5 square meters) per patient for 75% of all inpatients and 75% of outpatients whose length of stay exceeds four hours.
   c) A maximum of 30% of the provided areas can be located in interior atria, solaria, greenhouses, or conditioned spaces.
   d) The credit is only applicable to healthcare projects.

51) A new construction project team pursuing the Option 2: Financial Support part of the Site Development—Protect or Restore Habitat credit wants to calculate the amount of financial support that will be provided to a land trust. If the total site area of the project is 50,000 square feet, how much financial support should be provided to the land trust in order to earn the credit?
   a) $15,000
   b) $20,000
   c) $25,000
   d) $1,500

52) According to the SS credit Open Space, for projects that achieve a density of _____, extensive or intensive vegetated roofs can be used for the minimum 25% vegetation requirement, and the roof's physically accessible paving areas can be used toward credit compliance.
   a) A 0.5 floor-to-area ratio
   b) A 1.0 floor-to-area ratio
   c) A 1.5 floor-to-area ratio
   d) A 2.0 floor-to-area ratio

53) Which of the following statements is false about the Outdoor Water Use Reduction credit?
   a) If the project only uses xeriscaping, the credit can be earned through Option 1: No Irrigation Required.
   b) Additional reductions beyond the prerequisite level of 30% may be achieved with the use of any combination of efficiency, alternative water sources, and smart scheduling technologies.
   c) Nonvegetated surfaces, such as pavements, should be included in the landscape calculations.
   d) Alternative water sources to be used can include graywater, reclaimed wastewater, captured rainwater, and more.

54) For all the paths under the Option 1: Percentile of Rainfall Events part of the Rainwater Management credit, projects should manage the on-site rainwater runoff: (Choose two.)
   a) By using green infrastructure
   b) According to the National Climatic Data Center standards
   c) By using low-impact development
   d) By using a coordinated approach

55) Which of the following best describes the requirement for earning an exemplary performance point under the Construction and Demolition Waste Management credit?
   a) Diverting 100% of materials to include five material streams
   b) Pursuing any path under Option 1: Diversion in addition to Option 2: Reduction of Total Waste Material
   c) Pursing Path 1: Divert 50% and Three Material Steams in addition to Option 2: Reduction of Total Waste Material
   d) Pursing Path 2: Divert 75% and Four Material Steams in addition to Option 2: Reduction of Total Waste Material

56) Using which of the following roofing materials would cause the least heat island effect?
   a) Roofing material with a solar reflectance index (SRI) value of 90 and a three-year-aged SRI value of 80
   b) Roofing material with a solar reflectance index (SRI) value of 15 and a three-year-aged SRI value of 8
   c) Roofing material with a solar reflectance index (SRI) value of 50 and a three-year-aged SRI value of 47
   d) Roofing material with a solar reflectance index (SRI) value of 20 and a three-year-aged SRI value of 6

57) Per the SS credit Light Pollution Reduction, which of the following lighting types is not exempt from the credit's requirements?
   a) Government-mandated roadway lighting
   b) Video performance lighting used for theatrical purposes
   c) Specialized signal lighting for transportation
   d) Signage lighting

58) A team member of a LEED BD+C: New Construction project is preparing documentation for the LT credit Bicycle Facilities. Which of the following documentation is not required?
   a) A vicinity map showing the bicycle network and route and distance to eligible destinations
   b) A site plan showing bicycle storage locations
   c) A description of programs to support bicycle use
   d) Bicycle storage and shower room calculations

59) Which of the following statements is false regarding the Construction and Demolition Waste Management Planning prerequisite?
   a) Project teams should write down a final report showing all major waste streams generated, including their disposal and diversion rates.
   b) Project teams should implement the construction and demolition waste management plan and meet the target diversion rates defined in the prerequisite.
   c) Alternative daily cover (ADC) does not qualify as a material diverted from disposal.
   d) Hazardous materials (such as asbestos) cannot be diverted under the LEED requirements and are therefore exempt from the prerequisite's diversion calculations.

60) A project team is preparing a preliminary water budget analysis before the schematic design phase to calculate the project's water demand volume. Under which of the following credits is this required?
   a) Integrative Process credit
   b) Indoor Water Use Reduction credit
   c) Outdoor Water Use Reduction credit
   d) Water Metering credit

61) Which of the following rating systems is eligible for precertification?
   a) LEED BD+C: Hospitality
   b) LEED BD+C: Core and Shell
   c) LEED BD+C: New Construction and Major Renovations
   d) LEED BD+C: Retail

62) Per the Building-Level Energy Metering prerequisite, how long should projects commit to sharing their energy consumption and electrical demand data?
   a) For 5 years, starting from either the LEED certification date or typical occupancy
   b) For 5 years, starting from the typical occupancy date
   c) For 5 years, starting from the LEED certification date or typical occupancy, whichever comes first
   d) For 10 years, starting from the LEED certification date or typical occupancy, whichever comes first

63) A new construction project team pursuing the Option 1: Electric Vehicle Charging part of the Green Vehicles credit determines that the project has total parking capacity of 204 spaces. In order to earn the credit, how many of those parking spaces should contain an electric vehicle charging station (EVSE)?
a) 1
b) 2
c) 4
d) 5

64) A project team pursuing the Option 1: Flush-out part of the Indoor Quality Assessment credit is planning to perform the flush-out before the occupancy period. During the flush-out, how much air should be provided to the building?
a) 3,500 cubic feet of outdoor air per square foot of gross floor area
b) 7,500 cubic feet of outdoor air per square foot of gross floor area
c) 14,000 cubic feet of outdoor air per square foot of gross floor area
d) 20,000 cubic feet of outdoor air per square foot of gross floor area

65) In order to earn the most points under the Option 1: Diversion part of the Construction and Demolition Waste Management credit, project teams should do the following:
a) Divert 50% of the total construction and demolition material and three material streams
b) Divert 50% of the total construction and demolition material and four material streams
c) Divert 75% of the total construction and demolition material and three material streams
d) Divert 75% of the total construction and demolition material and four material streams

66) A 10-story mixed-use development project contains retail spaces on the first 5 floors and contains residential units on the floors above 5. If the gross floor area is the same on each story, which of the following rating systems can the project team use for the project?
a) Only LEED BD+C: Retail
b) Only LEED BD+C: New Construction and Major Renovation
c) The project team can either choose LEED BD+C: Retail or LEED BD+C: New Construction and Major Renovation
d) LEED BD+C: Retail and LEED BD+C: New Construction and Major Renovation rating systems should both be used

67) Under the Indoor Water Use Reduction prerequisite, by utilizing more efficient fixtures and fittings, how much reduction should be established from the baseline indoor water usage?
a) 10%
b) 20%
c) 30%
d) 40%

68) Under the Option 1: Environmental Product Declaration part of the Building Product Disclosure and Optimization—Environmental Product Declarations credit, project teams should use at least _____ different permanently installed products, sourced from at least _____ different manufacturers that meet one of the credit's disclosure criteria.
a) 10, 5
b) 10, 10
c) 20, 5
d) 20, 10

69) How many point(s) are awarded under the Innovation credit?
a) 1 point
b) 3 points
c) 4 points
d) 5 points

70) A project team is pursuing the Option 2: Leadership Extraction Practices part of the Building Product Disclosure and Optimization—Sourcing of Raw Materials credit. The team wants to calculate the contribution of a Forest Stewardship Council–certified wood product to the credit calculations. If the product is sourced within 80 miles of the project site and if the product costs $10,000, how much can this product be valued under the credit calculations?
a) $5,000
b) $8,000
c) $10,000
d) $20,000

71) Under the Thermal Comfort credit, a LEED BD+C: New Construction project should provide individual thermal comfort controls to at least the following:

a) 25% of the shared multioccupant spaces
b) 50% of the individual occupant spaces
c) 50% of the shared multioccupant spaces
d) 100% of the individual occupant spaces

72) Under the Option 2: Lighting Quality part of the Interior Lighting credit, projects should choose four of the eight strategies defined under the credit. Which of the following is not one of them?

a) Use light sources with a color rendering index (CRI) of 80 or higher for the entire project
b) Use lighting fixtures with a luminance of less than 2,500 cd/m2 between 45 and 90 degrees from nadir in the regularly occupied spaces
c) Provide individual lighting controls that enable occupants to adjust the lighting to suit their preferences
d) Use direct-only overhead lighting for 25% or less of the total connected lighting load for all regularly occupied spaces

73) According to the Option 1: Whole-Building Energy Simulation part of the Minimum Energy Performance prerequisite, how much energy improvement should new construction projects demonstrate in comparison with the baseline building performance?

a) 2%
b) 3%
c) 5%
d) 6%

74) Which of the following credits refers to the report called "Windows and Offices: A Study of Office Worker Performance and the Indoor Environment"?

a) Thermal Comfort
b) Quality Views
c) Interior Lighting
d) Acoustic Performance

75) A LEED AP suggests revising the project design in order to get more daylight inside the building and at the same time provide exterior views. Which of the following strategies can contribute to both?
   a) Designing a narrow floor plate
   b) Installing light shelves around the building perimeter
   c) Installing light tubes for the basement levels
   d) Increasing the area of tinted glazing around the building perimeter

76) Which of the following strategies would not make a contribution to the Heat Island Reduction credit?
   a) Providing shade with structures covered by energy generation systems
   b) Using an open-grid pavement system that is at least 50% unbound
   c) Increasing the area of vision glazing in the building facade
   d) Placing parking spaces under cover

77) Per the Option 2: Reduced Irrigation part of the Outdoor Water Use Reduction credit, project teams should reduce the project's landscape water consumption by at least _____ (1 point) or _____ (2 points) from the calculated baseline for the site's peak watering month.
   a) 30%, 50%
   b) 50%, 75 %
   c) 50%, 100%
   d) 75%, 100%

78) A new construction project pursuing the LT credit Access to Quality Transit wants to include a "planned" bus stop in the credit calculations. In which of the following cases can the "planned" bus stop be included?
   a) If the planned bus stop will be under construction at the time of the certificate of occupancy
   b) If the planned bus stop is sited, funded, and under construction at the time of the certificate of occupancy and will be completed within 24 months from that date
   c) If the planned bus stop will be funded within a year, will be under construction at the time of the certificate of occupancy, and will be completed within 30 months from that date
   d) If the planned bus stop is sited and will be completed within 36 months from the certificate of occupancy

79) According to the EA prerequisite Fundamental Commissioning and Verification, for a 100,000-square-foot commercial project, the qualified commissioning authority cannot be:
   a) A qualified employee of the owner
   b) An independent consultant
   c) An employee of the design or construction firm who is a part of the project design or construction team
   d) A disinterested subcontractor of the design or construction team

80) Under the Option 1: On-Site Restoration part of the Site Development—Protect or Restore Habitat credit, by using native or adapted vegetation, projects should restore the following:
   a) 10% (including the building footprint) of all portions of the site that were previously disturbed
   b) 20% (excluding the building footprint) of all portions of the site that were previously disturbed
   c) 30% (including the building footprint) of all portions of the site that were previously disturbed
   d) 30% (excluding the building footprint) of all portions of the site that were previously disturbed

81) Under the LT credit Bicycle Facilities, for all LEED BD+C projects except LEED BD+C: Schools, all the short-term bicycle storage provided should be within a _____ walking distance from any main entrance, and all the long-term bicycle storage should be within a 100-foot (30-meter) walking distance from any functional entry.
   a) 50-foot (15-meter)
   b) 75-foot (22-meter)
   c) 100-foot (30-meter)
   d) 150-foot (45-meter)

82) What is the minimum score that a vehicle should achieve on the American Council for an Energy Efficient Economy annual vehicle rating guide to be considered a green vehicle?
   a) 30
   b) 40
   c) 45
   d) 90

83) The commissioning authority is working on creating the commissioning plan to meet the requirements of the Fundamental Commissioning and Verification prerequisite. Which of the following is not required to be a part of that commissioning plan?
   a) Goals and objectives
   b) Systems to be commissioned
   c) Monitoring-based commissioning requirements
   d) Team member roles/responsibilities

84) Some LT credits require projects to provide preferred parking for some types of vehicles, such as green vehicles. Which of the following statements is true regarding the preferred parking location in LEED requirements?
   a) Preferred parking spaces should have the shortest walking distance to the main entrance of the building (inclusive of spaces designated for people with disabilities).
   b) Preferred parking spaces should have the shortest walking distance to the main entrance of the building (exclusive of spaces designated for people with disabilities).
   c) If parking is provided for a multilevel facility, the preferred parking spaces can be located on any level of the building.
   d) Preferred parking spaces should have the shortest walking distance to any functional entry of the building (exclusive of spaces designated for people with disabilities).

85) A LEED AP is working on the credit calculations of the EQ credit Quality Views to confirm that 75% of all the regularly occupied floor area meets at least two of the credit's four view criteria. Which of the following criteria is not one of them?
   a) Multiple lines of sight to vision glazing in different directions that are at least 90 degrees apart
   b) Views that include either flora, fauna, sky, or movement
   c) Unobstructed views located within the distance of three times the head height of the vision glazing
   d) Views with a view factor of 3 or greater, which is defined by "Windows and Offices: A Study of Office Worker Performance and the Indoor Environment"

86) Which of the following statements is false regarding the PBT Source Reduction—Mercury prerequisite?

   a) Newly constructed healthcare facilities cannot use mercury-containing equipment, including switching devices, thermostats, and other building system sources, with the exclusion of lamps.

   b) In the project's recycling collection system, project teams should identify the types of mercury-containing products and devices to be collected, identify the criteria for their handling by a recycling program, and identify the disposal methods for captured mercury.

   c) It is applicable to LEED BD+C: School and LEED BD+C: Healthcare projects.

   d) All healthcare projects should comply with 2010 FGI Guidelines for Design and Construction of Health Care Facilities, Section A1.3-4b, Mercury Elimination.

87) A project team decides to install a garden canopy covered by photovoltaic (PV) panels. Which of the following prerequisites/credits will this decision make a positive contribution to? (Choose three.)

   a) Optimize Energy Performance credit

   b) Minimum Energy Performance prerequisite

   c) Heat Island Reduction credit

   d) Renewable Energy Production credit

   e) Demand Response credit

88) Under the Option 2: Diverse Uses part of the Surrounding Density and Diverse Uses credit, a building's main entrance should be within _____ walking distance of the main entrance of four to seven (1 point) or eight or more (2 points) existing and publicly available diverse uses.

   a) Quarter-mile (0.4-km)

   b) Half-mile (0.8-km)

   c) Three-quarter-mile (1.2-km)

   d) One-mile (1.6-km)

89) Which of the following is the term used for the return of water to the atmosphere through evaporation from plants?

   a) Evapotranspiration

   b) Emissivity

   c) Embodied energy

   d) Mulching

90) Which of the following describes the information necessary to accomplish the owner's project requirements, including system descriptions, indoor environmental quality criteria, design assumptions, and references to applicable codes, standards, regulations, and guidelines?
   a) Owner's project requirements
   b) Basis of design
   c) Commissioning report
   d) Project submittals

91) How many Regional Priority credits are there for every project location?
   a) Two
   b) Four
   c) Six
   d) Eight

92) Under the Option 1: Innovation part of the Innovation credit, the proposed strategy for the innovation credit should meet the credit's criteria. Which of the following is not one of them?
   a) The proposed strategy should demonstrate a quantitative improvement in environmental performance.
   b) The strategy of the innovation credit should be comprehensive and should not address a limited portion of the project.
   c) The proposed innovation credit should have at least one component.
   d) The proposed strategy should be significantly better than standard sustainable design practices.

93) A residential project team aiming for LEED BD+C: New Construction certification wants to calculate compliance for the LT credit Bicycle Facilities. The project contains 100 residential units and 200 regular building occupants. How many long-term bicycle storage spaces should be installed in the project?
   a) 5
   b) 60
   c) 100
   d) 200

94) A LEED AP of a warehouse project is looking for ways to earn points from the Surrounding Density and Diverse Uses credit. In order to earn maximum points under Option 1: Development and Adjacency, which of the following strategies should the project team establish?

a) Locate the project on a previously developed site that was used for industrial purposes

b) Locate the project on a previously developed site that was used for commercial purposes

c) Construct or renovate the project on a site that is both a previously developed site and an adjacent site

d) Locate the project on a brownfield

95) Which of the following statements is false regarding the EQ credit Thermal Comfort?

a) Healthcare projects should provide individual thermal comfort controls for every patient room and at least 50% of the remaining individual occupant spaces.

b) Hospitality projects are not required to provide thermal comfort controls to the guest rooms under this credit.

c) The credit sets requirements for both thermal comfort design and thermal comfort controls.

d) Warehouses and distribution centers are exempt from thermal comfort design requirements.

96) Under the Daylight credit, projects pursuing any option should provide _____ glare control devices with manual overrides for all the regularly occupied spaces.

a) Only automatic

b) Only manual

c) Manual or automatic

d) Semi-automatic or automatic

97) A LEED AP is working on creating a plan that will meet the requirements of the Construction Indoor Air Quality Management Plan credit for a newly constructed residential project. Which of the following is not required to be addressed in the plan?

a) Meeting or exceeding all applicable control measures of the Sheet Metal and Air Conditioning National Contractors Association (SMACNA) IAQ Guidelines for Occupied Buildings under Construction

b) Protecting absorptive materials (installed or stored on-site) from moisture damage

c) Developing a plan based on the British Standard (BS 5228) to reduce noise emissions and vibrations from construction equipment and other nonroad engines

d) Prohibiting the use of tobacco products inside the building and within 25 feet (7.5 meters) of the building entrance during construction

98) Under the Option 2: Leadership Extraction Practices part of the Building Product Disclosure and Optimization—Sourcing of Raw Materials credit, project teams should use products that meet at least one responsible extraction criteria for at least _____.
   a) 25% (by volume) of the total value of permanently installed building products in the project
   b) 25% (by cost) of the total value of permanently installed building products in the project
   c) 30% (by weight) of the total value of permanently installed building products in the project
   d) 50% (by cost) of the total value of permanently installed building products in the project

99) Which of the following statements is false about the Indoor Quality Assessment credit?
   a) The flush-out should be completed in every space of the building.
   b) All interior finishes must be installed, and major VOC punch list items should be completed by the time flush-out is performed.
   c) If any partial work occurs during the flush-out in any space (such as installing furnishings), the flush-out process must be restarted from the beginning for that space.
   d) To earn the credit, project teams can choose to conduct an indoor air testing after the occupancy period instead of conducting a flush-out.

100)   The project team of a new construction project is evaluating different alternatives for choosing the right electric vehicle supply equipment (EVSE) for the LT credit Green Vehicles. Which of the following is not a required feature for the installed EVSE?
   a) Provide Level 2 charging capacity (208–240 volts) or greater
   b) Comply with the relevant regional or local standard for electrical connectors, such as SAE Surface Vehicle Recommended Practice J1772, SAE Electric Vehicle Conductive Charge Coupler
   c) Be networked or accessible from the Internet
   d) Be capable of refueling a number of vehicles per day equal to at least 2% of the total parking spaces

PRACTICE TEST 2 – ANSWERS

A score above 80 would indicate well preparation for the exam.

1	C	26	A	51	B	76	C
2	C	27	A	52	C	77	C
3	C	28	C	53	C	78	B
4	A	29	A	54	A and C	79	C
5	B	30	A	55	B	80	C
6	A and B	31	A	56	A	81	C
7	A	32	C	57	D	82	C
8	C	33	C	58	C	83	C
9	C	34	C	59	B	84	B
10	C	35	B	60	A	85	B
11	A	36	B	61	B	86	C
12	B	37	C	62	C	87	A, C, and D
13	B	38	A	63	D	88	B
14	C	39	A	64	C	89	A
15	D	40	B	65	D	90	B
16	C	41	A	66	C	91	C
17	A, B, and C	42	C	67	B	92	C
18	D	43	A	68	C	93	C
19	B	44	C	69	D	94	C
20	C	45	D	70	D	95	D
21	C	46	B	71	B	96	C
22	B	47	A	72	C	97	C
23	C	48	C	73	C	98	B
24	B	49	A	74	B	99	D
25	D	50	C	75	A	100	D

SECTION 5

PRACTICE TEST 2 ANSWERS & EXPLANATIONS

1) C

2) C
Under the Integrative Process credit, project teams should assess at least two strategies related to each of the following:

  - ➤ Site conditions: Evaluate shading, exterior lighting, landscaping, hardscape, and adjacent site conditions.
  - ➤ Massing and orientation: Evaluate and optimize the massing and orientation effect on the HVAC sizing, energy consumption, lighting, and renewable energy opportunities. Evaluate the number of floors, building footprint, and configuration.
  - ➤ Basic envelope attributes: Evaluate the wall and roof insulation values, thermal mass, glazing characteristics, window-to-wall ratios, shading, and window operability.

➤ Lighting levels: Evaluate interior surface reflectance values, lighting needs and levels in the occupied spaces, daylighting, high-efficiency lighting fixtures, and controls.

➤ Thermal comfort ranges: Evaluate thermal comfort range options and thermal comfort parameters.

➤ Plug and process load needs: Evaluate reducing plug and process loads through programmatic solutions such as equipment and purchasing policies, layout options, and more.

➤ **Programmatic and operational parameters: Evaluate multifunctioning spaces, space allotment per person, operating schedules, reduction of building area, and anticipated operations and maintenance.**

3) C

Under the Green Power and Carbon Offsets credit, projects should engage in a contract for **a minimum of 5 years**, to be delivered at least annually, from the qualified resources that have come online since January 1, 2005. The contract should specify the provision of at least 50% or 100% of the project's energy from green power, carbon offsets, and/or renewable energy certificates.

4) A

For LEED, "occupied spaces" are active spaces intended for human activity, such as private offices, dorm rooms, restrooms, or **corridors**. "Unoccupied spaces" are inactive spaces that are occupied occasionally for short periods of time, such as the **emergency exit corridor**, **mechanical rooms**, or **electrical rooms**.

5) B

No development can be made within 50 feet (15 meters) of wetlands, with the exception of some minor improvements. Sixty feet (18 meters) will satisfy this limit.

6) A and B

Under the Environmental Site Assessment prerequisite, project teams should conduct a Phase I Environmental Site Assessment in accordance with the ASTM E1527-05 standard or a local equivalent, and they should determine if any environmental contamination exists on-site.

And under the Option 3: Brownfield Remediation part of the High-Priority Site credit, in order to identify contamination, project teams need to conduct a Phase I or Phase II Environmental Site Assessment (or a local equivalent for projects outside the United States) or consult a biologist or environmental scientist.

Open Space and Integrative Process credits do not require conducting an environmental site assessment.

7) A
Under the Enhanced Commissioning credit, projects can get full points by selecting path 2 under option 1, in addition to option 2.

8) C
LEED BD+C: Warehouses and Distribution Centers projects basically have the same view requirements. However, those requirements are only applicable to the office portion of the building. For the bulk storage, sorting, and distribution areas, projects should meet the view requirements for only **25% of the regularly occupied floor area** (not 50%).

And only LEED BD+C: Healthcare projects have the opportunity to earn 2 points under this credit. If the inpatient units in the building meet the credit's view requirements, projects will earn 1 point. To earn the additional point, projects should configure the floor plan so that the floor area within 15 feet (4.5 meters) of the perimeter exceeds the perimeter area requirements and also complies with the credit's view requirements.

9) C

10) C
LEED refers to the Chartered Institution of Building Services Engineers (CIBSE) applications manual for <u>design calculations</u>.

11) A
The first step for LEED-certifying a building is to register the project through LEED Online, which means completing the registration form and paying the flat registration fee. In this phase, a LEED Project Administrator needs to be assigned.

A LEED Project Administrator is the primary project contact for the USGBC and GBCI. The LEED Project Administrator is the team member who acts as a project manager, overseeing the LEED project and organizing team members for certain tasks, credits, or prerequisites. The project administrator makes sure the LEED submission is complete and accurate before submitting the project to GBCI for review, and the project administrator accepts the review results once the review is complete. To avoid confusion, a LEED Project Administrator does not need to be a LEED Green Associate or a LEED AP. The duties of LEED Green Associates, LEED APs, and LEED Project Administrators in the project are completely different.

12) B

13) B

The Building Product Disclosure and Optimization—Material Ingredients credit refers to the GreenScreen v1.2 Benchmark. GreenScreen is a method used to identify chemicals of high concern and also safer alternatives to those chemicals. And since that credit is about analyzing the ingredients of a product, GreenScreen serves as a great tool.

14) C

The LEED Volume Program is a streamlined certification process for organizations that plan to certify **more than twenty-five prototype-based construction projects within three years**. An example of this would be a coffee-shop chain that plans to open up twenty-five coffee shops with uniform designs. Such a project could use the LEED Volume Program to pay lower certification fees to help streamline the certification process.

It is also important to mention that the LEED Campus Program, which is not for projects uniform in design but for multiple projects that are located on a single campus owned by the same entity. An example of this would be a university planning to construct several educational buildings on the same campus. These projects can use the LEED Campus Program to pay lower certification fees and streamline the certification process.

15) D

All the medical furnishings are not required to contain environmental product declarations under the Furniture and Medical Furnishings credit.

16) C

Under the Construction and Demolition Waste Management Planning prerequisite, projects should develop and implement a construction and demolition waste management plan by meeting the following:

- Establish waste diversion goals by identifying **at least five materials** (both structural and nonstructural) targeted for diversion. Make an approximate calculation to show the percentage of these materials compared to the total construction waste.
- Specify whether the materials will be separated or commingled and explain the diversion strategies planned. Describe how these materials will be transported to the recycling facilities and describe the recycling process.

17) A,B, and C

Under the Storage and Collection of Recyclables prerequisite, all LEED BD+C projects except LEED BD+C: Retail should take the necessary actions for safe collection, storage, and disposal of two of the following: **batteries, mercury-containing lamps**, and **electronic waste**.

LEED BD+C: Retail projects should conduct a waste stream analysis and identify a project's top five recyclable waste streams (by weight or volume) using consistent metrics throughout. Once the waste stream study is completed, project teams should list the top four recyclable waste streams and provide dedicated areas for separation, collection, and storage of the recyclables, which should also be accessible to waste haulers and building occupants.

18) D

In order to be eligible for this credit, the project has to be located inside a boundary of one of the following:

- LEED ND Pilot—Stage 2 LEED for Neighborhood Development Certified Plan
- LEED ND Pilot—Stage 3 LEED for Neighborhood Development Certified Project
- LEED 2009—Stage 2 Precertified LEED for Neighborhood Development Plan
- LEED 2009—Stage 3 LEED ND Certified Neighborhood Development
- LEED v4—LEED for Neighborhood Development Certified Plan
- LEED v4—LEED for Neighborhood Development Certified Built Project

If the project is inside the boundary of any of the following sites, no points will be awarded under this credit:

- LEED ND Pilot—Stage 1 LEED for Neighborhood Development Prereviewed Plan
- LEED 2009—Stage 1 Conditional Approval of LEED ND Plan
- LEED v4—LEED for Neighborhood Development Conditional Approval

19) B

Per the Green Power and Carbon Offsets credit, all the purchased carbon offsets should be **Green-e Climate-certified** or equivalent. On the other hand, the green power and renewable energy certificates (RECs) should be Green-e Energy-certified or the equivalent.

LEED refers to the EPA GreenChill for the best practices guideline for leak tightness at installation and for store certifications.

And Cradle to Cradle certification assesses the ingredients of a product, taking into account environmental and human health hazards, and it is referred to under the Building Product Disclosure and Optimization (BPDO)—Material Ingredients credit.

20) C

The Option 1: Historic Building Reuse part of the Building Life-Cycle Impact Reduction credit does not have any threshold for compliance. In other words, the credit does not define any area of the building to be reused or altered. <u>It only requires that the "historic" designation status of the building be still valid after the construction in accordance with the appropriate standards and agencies.</u> If the building's "historic" status is revoked after the historic review, this option can no longer be pursued. (In that case, project teams may pursue Option 3: Building and Material Reuse if they can meet its requirements.)

Additionally, project teams should not demolish any part of the historic building or the contributing building in a historic district unless it has structural problems or contains hazardous materials.

Any alteration, such as preservation, restoration, or rehabilitation, must be conducted in accordance with the local or national standards for rehabilitation wherever applicable.

For buildings listed locally, the approval for any demolition should be granted by the local historic preservation review board. For buildings listed in a state register or the US National Register of Historic Places, the approval for any demolition should be in a programmatic agreement with the state historic preservation office or National Park Service. Projects outside the United States can use the local equivalent agencies.

If the building is not subject to any historic review, the preservation professional must ensure conformance with the Secretary of Interior's Standards for the Treatment of Historic Properties (or a local equivalent for projects located outside the United States).

21) C

Passive solar is a type of solar power that deals with optimizing the project design to use sunlight more effectively. As it is a passive strategy, its function is not about generating energy from solar energy via equipment. Passive solar involves, for instance, orienting the building to maximize solar gains—using shades that do not allow summer sun but allow winter sun into the building—or creating thermal masses to store solar heat. However, under the Renewable Energy Production credit, projects should generate energy from renewable energy sources.

Under the Renewable Energy Production credit, eligible renewable energy sources contain photovoltaic, solar thermal, wind, biofuel, low-impact hydroelectricity, wave and tidal, and geothermal energy.

22) B

The use of glare control devices is required under the Daylight credit, such as **operable window blinds** or curtains. Projects pursuing any option should provide manual or automatic glare control devices with manual overrides for all the regularly occupied spaces.

Fixed-glare control devices—such as fixed exterior overhangs, fixed fins, fixed louvres, dark color glazing, frit glazing treatment, or additional glazing treatments—will not satisfy this credit. Acceptable glare control devices include interior window blinds, shades, curtains, movable exterior louvres, movable screens, and movable awnings.

23) C

Under the Option 2: Green Buses and School-Owned Vehicles part of the Green Vehicles credit, school projects should develop and implement a plan for every bus serving the school in order to meet the credit's emission standards within seven years of the building certificate of occupancy.

If there are any school buses that cannot meet these emission standards, the school project team should determine whether to retrofit or phase them out in order to meet these emission standards. If the school project team chooses to retrofit buses, the retrofitting must be approved by a relevant third party such as the **California Air Resources Board** or a local equivalent.

24) B

Under the **Construction Indoor Air Quality Management Plan credit**, project teams will need to regularly document their actions with site photographs to be uploaded to LEED Online. This is to demonstrate that the necessary actions were taken in the construction field to protect indoor air quality. An example of this would be the photographs of the HVAC ducts stored on-site with a protective covering to prevent construction dust entering inside.

25) D

If a developer is unfamiliar with green building practices, many municipalities provide free planning or certification training and assistance.

And in order to promote green developments, many municipalities award structural or financial incentives to developers or homeowners who practice green building techniques.

The structural incentives provide rewards for green building projects by making available additional density bonuses or expedited permitting processes. By reducing the review and permitting durations in exchange for developers' establishment of green building standards, municipalities encourage developers to design green buildings.

Density and height bonuses are another incentive. Many municipalities allow for percentage increases in floor-to-area ratio or other measures of density contingent upon certification or proof of green building practices.

The financial incentives are direct incentives in the form of tax credits or grants to developers that build green buildings. Some municipalities offer reductions or waivers for permit review or other less onerous permitting processes in exchange for developers' use of green building standards. Revolving loan funds can also be available to those seeking to build or renovate to green building standards.

26) A

Under the Low-Emitting Materials credit, flooring should comply with the **general emissions evaluation**, which requires products to be tested and determined compliant in accordance with the California Department of Public Health (CDPH) Standard Method v1.1-2010.

27) A

If the project meets the VOC requirements for <u>some</u> of the building materials under option 1 of the Low-Emitting Materials credit, the project teams can use the budget calculation method in option 2 to show that the overall VOC level in the building is less than the maximum threshold by calculating the weighted averages of each material's VOC level.

And one thing to mention is that, if furniture is in the project's scope of work, it cannot be excluded under the Low-Emitting Materials credit calculations.

28) C

See Appendix C — Prerequisites/Credits and Their Applicable Rating Systems.

29) A

Alternative compliance paths (ACPs) enable international projects to earn the appropriate prerequisites/credits by allowing them to meet international standards or their local standard instead of US-based standards.

After the project is registered in LEED Online, if a project team has questions about the technical details of a prerequisite, credit, or minimum program requirement (MPR), a credit interpretation ruling (CIR) is issued to ask for clarification. Sometimes the reference guide will not be able to provide all the information regarding the achievement of a particular prerequisite/credit, and in this case, the project team submits a CIR through LEED Online and asks for a clarification.

"Addenda" is the term that combines all the changes, improvements, issued LEED interpretations, and modifications made to a LEED rating system. Just like a piece of software updates itself once a week or so to incorporate the latest updates, LEED rating systems are updated with addenda.

Alternative credits do not exist.

30) A

Following is the table showing the refrigerants and their ozone depletion potentials (ODPs). In the table, note that natural refrigerants do not have any ozone depletion potential, and the ozone depletion potential for hydrofluorocarbons (HFCs) is very close to zero. Therefore, for this type of question, which compares the refrigerants' ODP values, if there aren't any natural refrigerants in the choices, HFCs will always be the answer.

Ozone Depletion and Global Warming Potentials of Common Refrigerants			
Refrigerant	**ODPr**	**GWPr**	**Common building application**
Chlorofluorocarbons			
CFC-11	1.0	4,680	Centrifugal chiller
CFC-12	1.0	10,720	Refrigerators, chiller
CFC-114	0.94	9,800	Centrifugal chiller
CFC-500	0.605	7,900	Centrifugal chiller, humidifier
CFC-502	0.221	4,600	Low-temp refrigeration
Hydrochlorofluorocarbon			
HCFC-22	0.04	1,780	Air conditioning, chiller
HCFC-123	0.02	76	CFC-11 replacement
Hydrofluorocarbons			
HFC-23	˜0	12,240	Ultra-low-temperature refrigeration
HFC-134a	˜0	1,320	CFC-12 or HCFC-22 replacement
HFC-245fa	˜0	1,020	Insulation agent, centrifugal chiller
HFC-404A	˜0	3,900	Low-temperature refrigeration
HFC-407C	˜0	1,700	HFC-22 replacement
HFC-410A	˜0	1,890	Air-conditioning
HFC-507A	˜0	3,900	Low-temperature refrigeration
Natural refrigerants			
Carbon dioxide (CO2)	0	1	
Ammonia (NH3)	0	0	
Propane	0	3	

31) A

"To support the design, construction, and eventual operation of a project that meets the owner's project requirements for energy, water, indoor environmental quality, and durability" is the intent of the Fundamental Commissioning and Verification prerequisite.

"To further support the design, construction, and eventual operation of a project that meets the owner's project requirements for energy, water, indoor environmental quality, and durability" is the intent of the Enhanced Commissioning and Verification credit.

"Maximize opportunities for integrated, cost-effective adoption of green design and construction strategies, emphasizing human health as a fundamental evaluative criterion for building design, construction and operational strategies. Utilize innovative approaches and techniques for green design and construction." This is the intent of the Integrative Project Planning and Design prerequisite.

32) C

33) C

Under this option, project teams should maintain at least **50%,** by surface area, of the existing building structure (for example, foundation, floor, roof decking), enclosure (for example, skin, framing), and interior structural elements (for example, walls, doors, floor coverings, ceiling systems) for buildings that meet local criteria of abandoned buildings or are considered blighted.

34) C

Increasing the vegetated area and reducing the pavement area will not affect the Reduced Parking Footprint credit, since pavement area will not affect the number of parking spaces in the project.

Increasing the vegetated area and reducing the hardscape area will have a positive effect on the Heat Island Reduction and Rainwater Management credits.

Increasing the area of vegetation will affect the outdoor water usage and therefore will also affect the Outdoor Water Use Reduction credit.

35) B

Projects need to provide preferred parking for carpools for **5%** of the total parking after the reductions have been made from the base ratios, not 10%.

To reinforce knowledge, below are the two cases under the credit:

Case 1: Baseline location
Projects that have not earned points under the Surrounding Density and Diverse Uses or Access to Quality Transit credits should achieve a 20% reduction from the base ratios.

Case 2: Dense and/or transit-served location
Projects that have earned 1 or more points under either the Surrounding Density and Diverse Uses credit or the Access to Quality Transit credit should achieve a 40% reduction from the base ratios.

In other words, if the project is in a dense and/or transit-served location, the project should further decrease its parking capacity from the base ratios of the Parking Consultants Council.

At last, projects without off-street parking will earn the credit automatically.

36) B

Under the Renewable Energy Production credit, points are awarded in accordance with the project's percentage of renewable energy use as shown in the following table:

Percentage of renewable energy	Points (except Core and Shell)	Points (Core and Shell)
1%	1	1
3%	—	2
5%	2	3
10%	3	—

37) C

For all the options under the Daylight credit, all LEED BD+C projects except healthcare should consider the regularly occupied floor area while the **LEED BD+C: Healthcare** projects should consider the perimeter area.

Perimeter floor area is the floor area within 15 feet (4.5 meters) of the perimeter. And it is important to note that this value is also necessary under the Quality Views credit calculations for the LEED BD+C: Healthcare projects.

To illustrate the "perimeter floor area", let's think about two design alternatives in which the first one is a square floor plan and the second one is a narrow-rectangle floor plan.

The square building will contain a big core area that will not be exposed to any views or daylight, and only the spaces at the perimeter will have access to outside views and daylight.

In the narrow-rectangle building, if the corridor is placed in the middle of the floor plan, all the rooms can have access to quality views or daylight. The following illustrations demonstrate the difference between these design alternatives. The white portions show the spaces with outside views or daylight, while the black areas are the spaces without any views or daylight. Note that the total floor area is the same in both of the design alternatives.

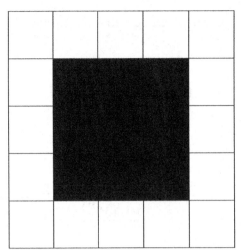

Square building configuration — 64% of the total floor area can have access to outside views or daylight

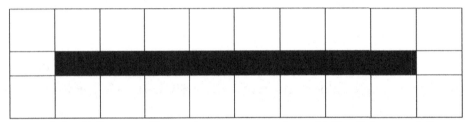

Narrow rectangle building configuration — more than 90% of the total floor area can have access to outside views or daylight

To summarize, the narrow rectangle building will contain more perimeter flor area as compared to the square building, even though they have the same total floor area.

However, it is also important to note that the initial cost of the narrow-rectangle building will be higher than the square building. Since the narrow-rectangle building has more perimeter length, the building will contain more exterior elements.

The same rule will apply to two buildings with the same configuration but with different floor areas. If the total floor area of the narrow-rectangle building in the previous illustration increases (while maintaining the ratio), the total area with access to outdoor views will also decrease.

This is the reason that the floor area and the floor layout are the top priorities to consider when designing for daylight and quality views.

38) A

39) A

Under the Fundamental Refrigerant Management prerequisite, existing small HVAC&R equipment or other equipment, such as standard refrigerators and small water cooler units containing less than **0.5 pound (225 grams)** of refrigerant, are exempt from the prerequisite requirements.

40) B

There are several rules that LEED requires while counting diverse uses. First, the same type of store cannot be counted more than twice. For example, if there are four supermarkets within walking distance, they can only be counted as two diverse uses.

Second, **a diverse-use outlet selling products in several categories can only be counted as one diverse use**. For example, a retail store that contains a pharmacy and a supermarket within the same store cannot be counted as two diverse uses.

Finally, the counted diverse uses must be present under at least three of the five diverse use categories, exclusive of the building's primary use.

Project teams can also count the planned but currently not-operating diverse uses, but each diverse use must be active within one year of the date when the project accepts its initial certificate of occupancy.

As is the case with all walking-distance calculations, projects should confirm walkability on a map by the use of paths that provide a safe and comfortable environment for pedestrians and provide a continuous network of sidewalks.

41) A

ASHRAE 52.2-2007 is related to air filters. ASHRAE standard 55-2010 is a standard on thermal comfort conditions for human occupancy. ASHRAE standard 170-2008 is used to address the mechanical ventilation requirements of healthcare projects. CIBSE Applications Manual AM10 is used for natural ventilation strategies.

42) C

Under the Advanced Energy Metering credit, project teams should install advanced energy metering for the following:
- All whole-building energy sources used by the building
- Any individual energy end uses that consume **10% or more** of the total annual consumption of the building

43) A

Under the Demand Response credit, if there is a demand response program available for the project's location, with the intention of multiyear renewal, projects should enroll in a **minimum one-year** DR program for at least 10% of the estimated peak electricity demand.

44) C

Under the Low-Emitting Materials credit requirements for **furniture evaluation**, new furniture and furnishings should be tested in accordance with the ANSI/BIFMA Standard Method M7.1-2011 and meet the ANSI/BIFMA e3-2011 Furniture Sustainability Standard Sections 7.6.1 and 7.6.2.

45) D

The ANSI/ASHRAE/IESNA Standard 90.1.-2010, Appendix G, with errata is used for the whole-building energy simulation under the Option 1: Whole-Building Energy Simulation part of the Minimum Energy Performance prerequisite and the Optimize Energy Performance credit.

46) B

47) A

In some Indoor Environmental Quality prerequisites/credits, the spaces inside the building are categorized as "occupied spaces" or as "unoccupied spaces." Furthermore, "occupied spaces" are further categorized as "regularly occupied spaces" or as "nonregularly occupied spaces."

For LEED, "occupied spaces" are active spaces intended for human activity, such as private offices, dorm rooms, restrooms, or corridors. "Unoccupied spaces" are inactive spaces that are occupied occasionally for short periods of time, such as the emergency exit corridor, mechanical rooms, or electrical rooms.

When further categorizing the "occupied spaces" as "regularly occupied spaces" or as "nonregularly occupied spaces," the duration of occupancy is considered. **"Regularly occupied spaces" are spaces where people spend time of more than one hour of continuous occupancy per person per day on average.** If a space is not used daily, but people spend more than one hour when using that space, it should still be considered "regularly occupied space." Examples of regularly occupied spaces would be auditoriums, private offices, dorm rooms, meeting rooms, or reception desks.

"Nonregularly occupied spaces" are types of spaces that do not meet the definition of "regularly occupied spaces." Examples of "nonregularly occupies spaces" would be corridors, locker rooms, or stairways.

In some credits, "occupied spaces" also need to be categorized as "individual occupant spaces" or as "shared multioccupant spaces" based on the number of occupants using the space and their activities. An "individual occupant space" is a type of space where a person performs distinct tasks, such as a private office, reception desk, or hotel guest room. On the other hand, the "shared multioccupant space" is a type of space where people pursue collaborative and overlapping tasks, such as a gymnasium, classroom, meeting room, hotel lobby, or auditorium.

48) C

In order to pursue option 3 of the Minimum Energy Performance prerequisite, a project should be less than 100,000 square feet (9,290 square meters), and the project should not be a <u>school</u>, <u>healthcare facility</u>, <u>warehouse</u>, or <u>laboratory</u>.

However, one important thing to note is that a project pursuing option 3 will not be eligible to pursue the Optimize Energy Performance credit. That credit is basically a continuation of this prerequisite, and it does not contain an option 3.

49) A

To pursue the maximum number of points in the Optimize Energy Performance credit, project teams will need to choose Option 1: Whole-Building Energy Simulation since it contains the most points (18 points). Option 2: Prescriptive Compliance: ASHRAE Advanced Energy Design Guide contains 6 points.

And project teams that will pursue option 1 of the credit should also pursue option 1 of the Minimum Energy Performance prerequisite and create an energy model to be used for both that prerequisite and the Optimize Energy Performance credit.

50) C

According to the Direct Exterior Access credit, as its name implies, no interior space qualifies, and projects should provide direct exterior access. Only under the Places of Respite credit, a maximum of 30% of the respite area can be located in interior atria, solaria, greenhouses, or conditioned spaces.

51) B

Under the Option 2: Financial Support part of the Site Development—Protect or Restore Habitat credit, project teams should provide financial support equivalent to at least $0.40 per square foot ($4 per square meter) for the total site area, including the building footprint. And this financial support must be provided to a land trust or conservation organization within the same EPA Level III ecoregion or the project's state.

For this question, the amount of financial support provided to the land trust should be:

$$50,000 \times \$0.40 = \mathbf{\$20,000}$$

52) C

53) C

Nonvegetated surfaces, such as pavements, are always **excluded** (not included), from landscape calculations, as they are unrelated to potable water consumption. Athletic fields, vegetated playgrounds, and food gardens may be included or excluded from these calculations at the project team's decision.

Also, additional reductions beyond the prerequisite level of 30% may be achieved with the use of any combination of efficiency, alternative water sources, and smart scheduling technologies. However, under the Outdoor Water Use Reduction prerequisite, note that project teams cannot use alternative water sources (such as reclaimed water, graywater, or harvested rainwater) to establish the 30% outdoor water reduction.

Alternative water sources can include graywater, reclaimed wastewater, swimming pool backwash water, captured rainwater, refrigeration system condensate, fluid cooler discharge, food steamer discharge, fire pump test water, industrial process water, municipally supplied treated wastewater, stormwater and foundation drain water, and ice machine condensate.

54) A and C

55) B

Expect to see a question regarding exemplary performance points on the exam. To qualify for an exemplary performance point under the Construction and Demolition Waste Management credit, projects can pursue any path under Option 1: Diversion in addition to Option 2: Reduction of Total Waste Material.

56) A

The solar reflectance index value of a material is measured from a scale of 0 to 100, and within that scale, light-colored materials are closer to scoring a 100 SRI while darker-colored materials are closer to scoring a 0 SRI. Thus, the higher the SRI or SR, the lower the heat island effect. That being said, a roofing material with an SRI value of 90 and a three-year-aged SRI value of 80 will cause the least heat island effect compared with the other roofing materials in other choices.

57) D

Below are the types of lighting that are exempt from the credit requirements if they are controlled separately from the nonexempt lighting:
- Specialized signal, directional, and marker lighting for transportation
- Lighting solely used for facade and landscape lighting in MLO lighting zones 3 and 4 and that is automatically turned off from midnight to 6:00 a.m.
- Government-mandated roadway lighting
- Lighting for theatrical purposes, stages, and video performances
- Hospital emergency department and helipad lighting
- National flag lighting in MLO lighting zones 2, 3, or 4

Internally illuminated exterior signage has its own set of requirements under this credit. Any internally illuminated exterior signage should not exceed a luminance of **200 cd/m²** (nits) **during nighttime hours** and **2,000 cd/m²** (nits) **during daytime hours**.

58) C
Documenting the description of programs to support bicycle use is applicable to LEED BD+C: Retail projects since retail projects are required to provide a bicycle maintenance program for employees or bicycle route assistance for employees and customers.

59) B
The Construction and Demolition Waste Management Planning prerequisite encourages the project teams to create a construction and demolition waste management plan to identify potential strategies for reducing the generation of construction waste. However, it does not define any target diversion rates.

However, this prerequisite also has a credit called the Construction and Demolition Waste Management credit. And if the project teams choose to implement the construction and demolition waste management plan by meeting the target diversion rates defined in the credit, then the credit can be earned in accordance with the diversion rates that have been met. In fact, this prerequisite does not force implementation of a developed waste management plan with the target diversion rates set forth by the USGBC; rather, it only asks the project teams to create a plan, which includes their targets, and a final report showing the total waste versus amount of diverted and disposed of waste. In other words, there is no minimum threshold for diversion in this prerequisite. However, if the project teams aim for the Construction and Demolition Waste Management credit, their CWM plan created under this prerequisite should also address that credit's threshold levels.

It's also important to note that alternative daily cover (ADC) does not qualify as a material diverted from disposal in LEED calculations. (Even though ADC will not count as a diversion, it should still be included as a portion of the total construction waste generated.) And land-cleaning debris, which is created by the removal of rock, soil, stone, and vegetation, is not considered waste since the ingredients are all natural products. However, the handling of both alternative daily cover and land-cleaning debris, as well as all the other materials not contributing to diversion, should still be addressed in the construction and demolition waste management plan.

Also, hazardous materials, such as asbestos, cannot be diverted under the LEED requirements and are therefore exempt from these calculations.

60) A

Under the **Integrative Process credit**, projects should perform a preliminary water budget analysis before completing the schematic design and should calculate the project's water demand volume. Next, project teams should look for strategies for reducing the potable water consumption, including assessment of the nonpotable water sources.

If a project team decides to pursue this credit, a preliminary water budget analysis will be a good starting point to evaluate all the alternatives for reducing the building's potable water demand. This will also contribute to the Indoor Water Use Reduction and Outdoor Water Use Reduction credits. However, the Indoor Water Use Reduction and Outdoor Water Use Reduction credits do not require a preliminary water budget analysis.

61) B

The LEED BD+C: Core and Shell rating system is eligible for precertification. Once the developer has established a goal to develop a LEED BD+C: Core and Shell project, the USGBC will grant precertification to aid in marketing the project to potential tenants and financiers for the unique and valuable green features of the proposed building. Precertification will be granted after the USGBC reviews the early design documents of the project. However, precertification will not guarantee LEED certification since LEED certification will be given only at the end of construction, when all the requirements are met.

62) C

63) D

Under the Option 1: Electric Vehicle Charging part of the Green Vehicles credit, new construction projects should install electric vehicle supply equipment in 2% of all the parking spaces used by the project. Those spaces should also be identified and reserved for sole use by plug-in electric vehicles. The following is the calculation to find the number of parking spaces with EVSE:

$$204 \times 0.02 = 4.08\text{—rounded up—}\textbf{5 spaces with EVSE}$$

Note that in this type of credit calculation, numbers are rounded up, not down.

64) C

65) D

In order to earn the most points under the Option 1: Diversion part of the Construction and Demolition Waste Management credit, projects should choose path 2 and divert **at least 75%**

of the total construction and demolition material. Diverted materials should include **at least four material streams**.

66) C

In LEED, projects cannot be divided into different rating systems with respect to sections, and the whole project should be certified under one rating system. If the project seems applicable to more than one rating system, the 40/60 rule should be used to decide on the rating system.

Under the 40/60 rule, a project should be divided into sections in accordance with the appropriate rating system each section fits. Then, the total floor area corresponding to each rating system should be calculated. If the total floor area of one of the applicable rating systems is less than 40% of the project's total floor area, that rating system cannot be used. If the total floor area of one of the applicable rating systems is more than 60% of the project's total area, that rating system must be used. If it falls between 40% and 60%, then the project team can decide on the rating system to be used for the project.

For this question, since 50% of the project is applicable to LEED BD+C: Retail, and the other 50% is applicable to LEED BD+C: New Construction and Major Renovation, **the project team can choose which rating system to use**.

67) B

68) C

Under the Option 1: Environmental Product Declaration part of the Building Product Disclosure and Optimization—Environmental Product Declarations credit, project teams should use at least **20** different permanently installed products sourced from at least **five** different manufacturers that meet one of the following disclosure criteria:

- **Product-specific declarations**: Only the products with a publicly available, critically reviewed life-cycle assessment conforming to ISO 14044 and having at least a cradle to gate scope assessment will qualify under these criteria. For the purposes of credit-achievement calculations, these products will be valued as one-quarter (1/4) of a product.
- **Environmental Product Declarations**: To qualify for an EPD, a product must conform to ISO 14025, 14040, 14044, and EN 15804 or ISO 21930, and the EPD should have at least a cradle to gate scope assessment. Next, for the purposes of credit achievement calculations, the EPDs will be valued in accordance with their types as follows:

    a. Industry-wide (generic) Type III third-party certification EPD: This includes products with industry-wide (generic) Type III third-party certification (including external certification that the manufacturer is recognized as the participant by the program operator). These products will be valued as one-half (1/2) of a product for the purposes of credit-achievement calculations.

b. <u>Product-specific Type III third-party certification EPD</u>: This includes products with product-specific Type III third-party certification (including external certification that the manufacturer is recognized as the participant by the program operator). These products will be valued as one whole (1) product for the purposes of credit achievement calculations.

➤ **Other USGBC-approved programs**: This category includes products that comply with other USGBC-approved environmental product declaration frameworks.

69) D

70) D

Under the Option 2: Leadership Extraction Practices part of the Building Product Disclosure and Optimization—Sourcing of Raw Materials credit, Forest Stewardship Council (FSC)–certified wood products are valued at 100% of their cost in the credit-achievement calculation. Additionally, in the credit-achievement calculations, materials sourced (extracted, manufactured, or purchased) within 100 miles (160 kilometers), which is the location valuation factor of LEED, of the project site will be valued at 200% of the base contributing cost. With this information, we first need to multiply the cost of the product with the FSC-certified product valuation factor. Next, this value will be multiplied with the location valuation factor.

$10,000 x 100% (FSC-certified product valuation factor) = $10,000

$10,000 x 200% (location valuation factor) = **$20,000**

71) B

Under the Thermal Comfort credit, LEED BD+C: New Construction projects should provide <u>individual</u> thermal comfort controls to at least **50% of the individual occupant spaces**. Additionally, projects should provide group thermal comfort controls for <u>all</u> shared multioccupant spaces.

72) C

Providing individual lighting controls that enable occupants to adjust the lighting to suit their preferences is addressed under the Option 1: Lighting Control part of the Interior Lighting credit. As the name implies, Option 2: Lighting Quality deals with the lighting quality rather than the lighting controls.

Under option 2, project teams should choose four of the following eight strategies.

1. Use lighting fixtures with a luminance of less than 2,500 cd/m² between 45 and 90 degrees from nadir in the regularly occupied spaces. (Wallwash fixtures properly aimed at walls, indirect uplighting fixtures, and any other specific applications such as adjustable fixtures are excluded).

2. Use light sources with a color rendering index (CRI) of 80 or higher for the entire project. (Lamps or fixtures specifically designed to use color lighting for effect, site lighting, and any other special-use lighting are exempt.)

3. For at least 75% of the total connected lighting load, use light sources that have a rated life (or L70 for LED sources) of at least 24,000 hours (at 3 hours per start, if applicable).

4. Use direct-only overhead lighting for 25% or less of the total connected lighting load for all regularly occupied spaces.

5. For at least 90% of the regularly occupied floor area, projects should meet or exceed the following thresholds for area-weighted average surface reflectance: 85% for ceilings, 60% for walls, and 25% for floors.

6. Select furniture (if included in the scope of work) should meet the following thresholds for area-weighted average surface reflectance: 45% for work surfaces and 50% for movable partitions.

7. For at least 75% of the regularly occupied floor area, the ratio of average wall surface illuminance (excluding fenestration) to average work surface illuminance should not exceed 1:10. Projects must also meet strategy 5, strategy 6, or demonstrate an area-weighted surface reflectance of at least 60% for walls.

8. For at least 75% of the regularly occupied floor area, the ratio of average ceiling illuminance (excluding fenestration) to work surface illuminance should not exceed 1:10. Projects must also meet strategy 5, strategy 6, or demonstrate an area-weighted surface reflectance of at least 85% for ceilings.

73) C

74) B

Under the **Quality Views** credit, 75% of all regularly occupied floor area must meet at least two of the following four view criteria:

➤ Multiple lines of sight to vision glazing in different directions that are at least 90 degrees apart.

➤ Views that include at least two of the following:

a) Flora, fauna, or sky

b) Movement

c) Objects at least 25 feet (7.5 meters) from the exterior of the glazing

👈 Unobstructed views located within the distance of three times the head height of the vision glazing.

👈 Views with a view factor of 3 or greater, which is defined by **"Windows and Offices: A Study of Office Worker Performance and the Indoor Environment."**

75) A

Think about two design alternatives in which the first one is a square floor plan and the second one is a narrow-rectangle floor plan. The square building will contain a big core area that will not be exposed to any views, and only the spaces at the perimeter will have access to outside views and daylight. In the narrow-rectangle building, if the corridor is placed in the middle of the floor plan, all the rooms can have access to quality views and daylight. The following illustrations demonstrate the difference between these design alternatives. The white portions show the spaces with outside views, while the black areas are the spaces without any views. Note that the total floor area is the same in both of the design alternatives.

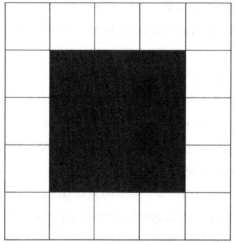

Square building configuration — 64% of the total floor area can have access to outside views and daylight

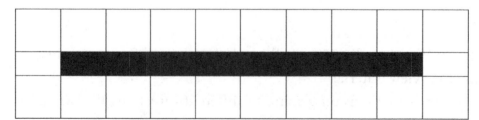

Narrow rectangle building configuration — more than 90% of the total floor area can have access to outside views and daylight

Continuing by explaining the other choices, light shelves are horizontal, light-reflecting overhangs that are positioned to reflect the daylight into the desired area of the building. However, they will not provide exterior views.

Light tubes, also called sun tubes or sun pipes, are structures that are used to transport sunlight inside a building. To illustrate, imagine a big pipe with a reflective inside surface that goes through the roof to the ceiling of a room. It captures the sunlight on the roof and transports it inside the pipe all the way down to the room. But again, they will not provide any exterior views.

Using more glazing will surely provide both daylight and exterior views, however, tinted glazing will block this effect. This is the reason that tinted glazing is not accepted under the Quality Views credit. According to the LEED requirements, glazing should allow a clear image of outdoors and should also be free of frits, patterns, fibers, or tints that disturb color.

76) C

Under the Heat Island Reduction credit, for the "non-roof measures" on-site, the credit requires projects to:

- ➣ Use existing plants or install new plants that will provide shade over paving areas on the site within 10 years of planting. Install vegetated planters. However, plants must be in place at the time of the occupancy permit, and artificial turf cannot be included.
- ➣ **Provide shade with structures covered by energy generation systems** (for example, solar thermal collectors, photovoltaics, wind turbines, etc.).
- ➣ Provide shade with architectural devices or structures that have a three-year aged solar reflectance value of at least 0.28. If this information is not available, projects can use materials with an initial SR of at least 0.33.
- ➣ Provide shade with vegetated structures.
- ➣ Use paving materials with a three-year aged solar reflectance value of at least 0.28. If this information is not available, the projects can use materials with an initial SR of at least 0.33.
- ➣ **Use an open-grid pavement system that is at least 50% unbound.**

Also, placing parking spaces under cover would contribute to Option 2: Parking Under Cover. However, increasing the area of vision glazing in the building exterior would not make any contribution to the Heat Island Reduction credit. Thus, increasing the area of vision glazing can contribute to the Daylight and Quality Views credits.

77) C

78) B

"Planned" stops or stations are those stops or stations that are planned but at the time are nonoperational and can be counted under the Access to Quality Transit credit if they're sited, funded, and under construction at the time of the certificate of occupancy and will be completed within **24 months** from that date.

79) C

Under the Fundamental Commissioning and Verification prerequisite, the CxA can be:
- A qualified employee of the owner
- An independent consultant
- An employee of the design or construction firm who is <u>not</u> a part of the project design or construction team (except that for projects smaller than 20,000 square feet, the CxA can be a qualified member of the design or construction team as well)
- A disinterested subcontractor of the design or construction team
- A qualified member of the design or construction team for small projects with computer room peak cooling loads of less than 2,000,000 Btu/h (600 kW) or a total computer room peak cooling load of less than 600,000 Btu/h (175 kW)

80) C

81) C

Under the Bicycle Facilities credit, all the short-term bicycle storage provided should be within a **100-foot (30-meter)** walking distance from any main entrance, and all the long-term bicycle storage should be within a 100-foot (30-meter) walking distance from any functional entry. Regarding only schools, all the long-term bicycle storage provided should be within a 100-foot (30-meter) walking distance from any main entrance (as opposed to a functional entry), and school projects will not provide any short-term bicycle storage.

82) C

83) C

Monitoring-based commissioning takes place under the Enhanced Commissioning credit, not the Fundamental Commissioning and Verification prerequisite.

Under the Fundamental Commissioning and Verification prerequisite, with the engagement of the commissioning authority (CxA), the CxA will develop a **commissioning plan** to outline the whole Cx process and review the OPR, the BOD, and the design documents.

The Cx plan will contain the following:

- ➤ Goals and objectives
- ➤ Systems to be commissioned
- ➤ Team member roles/responsibilities
- ➤ OPR reviews
- ➤ BOD reviews
- ➤ Development of functional tests
- ➤ Verification of system performance
- ➤ Reporting of deficiencies and acceptance of building systems

84) B

The preferred parking spaces should have the shortest walking distance to the main entrance of the building (exclusive of spaces designated for people with disabilities).

If parking is provided for a multilevel facility, the preferred spaces should be located on the level that is closest to the main entrance of the building. If there are different parking areas for different kinds of building users (customer parking, staff parking, etc.), then a project either can distribute the required preferred parking spaces proportionally across each different type of parking area, or it can provide one general preferred parking zone with enough parking space for all user types and can still separate the remaining parking spaces by user type.

85) B

Views that only include flora, fauna, sky, or movement will not satisfy the credit's view requirements; there should be more than one element. Under the Quality Views credit, 75% of all the regularly occupied floor area must meet at least two of the following four view criteria:

- ➤ Multiple lines of sight to vision glazing in different directions that are at least 90 degrees apart.
- ➤ Views that include **at least two** (not one) of the following:

  - ▪ Flora, fauna, or sky
  - ▪ Movement
  - ▪ Objects at least 25 feet (7.5 meters) from the exterior of the glazing

- ➤ Unobstructed views located within the distance of three times the head height of the vision glazing. (To satisfy this requirement, the project team will first determine the head height of the vision glazing for each regularly occupied space. Next, in the floor plan, the team will identify all the regularly occupied floor area that is within three times the head height of the perimeter. This area should not contain any obstruction.)
- ➤ Views with a view factor of 3 or greater, which is defined by "Windows and Offices: A Study of Office Worker Performance and the Indoor Environment." ("View factor" is a

measure of the amount and quality of the outdoor views within a 90-degree cone of vision from an individual workstation. A view factor of 5 represents a high-quality view, and a view factor of 0 represents a poor-quality view.)

86) C

The PBT Source Reduction—Mercury prerequisite is only applicable to LEED BD+C: Healthcare projects and not to LEED BD+C: School projects.

In the project's recycling collection system, the project team should identify the types of mercury-containing products and devices to be collected, identify the criteria for their handling by a recycling program, and identify the disposal methods for captured mercury.

Additionally, all healthcare projects should comply with 2010 FGI Guidelines for Design and Construction of Health Care Facilities, Section A1.3-4b, Mercury Elimination, as outlined in the following points:

- New construction projects: Healthcare facilities cannot use mercury-containing equipment, including switching devices, thermostats, and other building system sources, with the exclusion of lamps.
- Renovation projects: Healthcare facilities should develop a phase-out plan to eliminate mercury-containing products and upgrade current mercury-containing lamps to high-efficiency, mercury-free, or low-mercury lamp technology.

87) A, C, and D

Under the Option 1: Whole-Building Energy Simulation part of the Minimum Energy Performance prerequisite, the percent improvement in the baseline building performance must be established without considering the on-site renewable energy sources (such as PV panels for this question). However, on-site renewable energy sources can be counted toward energy savings under the Optimize Energy Performance credit.

Installing a canopy covered by PV panels will also contribute to the Heat Island Reduction credit because providing shade with structures covered by energy generation systems (for example, solar thermal collectors, photovoltaics, wind turbines, etc.) is one of the "nonroof" strategies under that credit.

Since installing PV panels will result in producing on-site renewable energy, this will also contribute to the Renewable Energy Production credit.

However, installing PV panels will not contribute to the Demand Response credit.

88) B

89) A

Emissivity (infrared or thermal emittance) is a measure that shows how much heat or infrared radiation a material can shed back into the atmosphere.

Embodied energy is the total energy consumed resulting from a product's manufacturing, transportation, installation, use, and disposal.

And mulching is a protective layer applied to the surface of soil that will help to keep the roots of the plants cool and therefore prevent evaporation.

90) B

91) C

There are **six** available Regional Priority credits for every location. And one point will be awarded for each Regional Priority credit achieved, up to a maximum of four.

92) C

The proposed strategy to get the innovation credit should meet the following criteria:

- ➤ Demonstrate a quantitative improvement in environmental performance. In other words, the project should establish a baseline of standard performance and compare the final design performance with the baseline.
- ➤ The strategy of the innovation credit should be comprehensive and should not address a limited portion of the project. In addition, **the proposed strategy for the innovation credit should have at least two (not one) components** and should not be limited to the use of a particular product or design strategy.
- ➤ Finally, the proposed strategy should be significantly better than standard sustainable design practices.

93) C

Residential projects should provide short-term bicycle storage for at least 2.5% of all peak visitors (cannot be fewer than four spaces per building) and provide long-term bicycle storage for at least 30% of all the regular building occupants, which <u>cannot be less than one storage space per residential unit</u>. In this case, long-term bicycle storage needed for 30% of all the regular building occupants would be:

Long-term bicycle storage: $200 \times 0.3 = 60$ spaces < 100 spaces

However, for residential projects, the amount of long-term bicycle storage cannot be less than one storage space per residential unit. This means that the project team will need to provide

100 long-term bicycle storage spaces instead of 60.

94) C

Under the Option 1: Development and Adjacency part of the Surrounding Density and Diverse Uses credit, project teams should construct or renovate the project site on a previously developed site that was used for industrial or commercial purposes (2 points). Or they should construct or renovate the project on a site that is made up of both a previously developed site and an adjacent site; the adjacent sites must be used at the time for industrial or commercial purposes (3 points).

95) D

For the office portions of the building (not for the whole building), LEED BD+C: Warehouses and Distribution Centers projects should meet the credit's requirements for thermal comfort design just like the other rating systems.

Additionally, for the regularly occupied spaces of the building's bulk storage, sorting, and distribution areas, project teams should implement one or more of the following design alternatives:
- Radiant flooring
- Circulating fans
- Passive systems, such as heat venting, nighttime air, or wind flow
- Localized active cooling (refrigerant- or evaporative-based systems) or heating systems
- Localized, hard-wired fans that provide air movement for occupants' comfort
- Other equivalent thermal comfort strategies

96) C

97) C

Under the Construction Indoor Air Quality Management Plan credit, "developing a plan based on the British Standard (BS 5228) to reduce noise emissions and vibrations from construction equipment and other nonroad engines" is a requirement for LEED BD+C: Healthcare projects, not for LEED BD+C: New Construction projects.

98) B

Under the Option 2: Leadership Extraction Practices part of the Building Product Disclosure and Optimization—Sourcing of Raw Materials credit, project teams should use products that meet at least one of the following responsible extraction criteria for at least **25% (by cost) of the total value of permanently installed building products in the project:**

- <u>Extended producer responsibility (EPR)</u>: This includes products purchased from a manufacturer that is involved in an extended-producer-responsibility program or is directly responsible for extended producer responsibility.
- <u>Biobased materials</u>: Biobased products that meet the Sustainable Agriculture Network's Sustainable Agriculture Standard. Biobased raw materials must be tested using ASTM Test Method D6866 and be legally harvested. Hide products, such as leather and other animal skin material, are excluded.
- <u>Wood products</u>: Wood products must be certified by the Forest Stewardship Council (FSC) or another USGBC-approved equivalent.
- <u>Materials reuse</u>: This criterion includes salvaged, refurbished, or reused products.
- <u>Recycled content</u>: These products must conform to ISO 14021-1999.

Any other USGBC-approved program: Any other USGBC-approved program meeting leadership extraction criteria can be used.

99) D

Under the Option 2: Air Testing part of the Indoor Quality Assessment credit, project teams will need to conduct air testing to determine if the contamination levels are above or below the credit's threshold values. If the contamination exceeds the credit's threshold values, project teams should clear the contamination and conduct another test.

However, indoor air quality testing should take place <u>before occupancy</u>, not after occupancy.

100) D

Under the Option 2: Liquid, Gas, or Battery Facilities part of the Green Vehicles credit, projects should install liquid or gas alternative fuel fueling facilities or a battery switching station that should be capable of refueling a number of vehicles per day equal to at least 2% of the total parking spaces.

However, installing EVSE is addressed under Option 1: Electric Vehicle Charging. And under this option, projects should install electric vehicle supply equipment in 2% of all the parking spaces used by the project.

Additionally, the installed EVSE should have the following properties:

- Provide Level 2 charging capacity (208–240 volts) or greater
- Comply with the relevant regional or local standard for electrical connectors, such as SAE Surface Vehicle Recommended Practice J1772, SAE Electric Vehicle Conductive Charge Coupler, or for projects outside the United States, IEC 62196 of the International Electrotechnical Commission
- Be networked or accessible from the Internet (must have Wi-Fi, a cellular modem, or other capability to send usage data to a server) and be capable of participating in a demand-response program or time-of-use pricing to encourage off-peak charging.

SECTION 6

PRACTICE TEST 3

These practice tests have been prepared in the same format and with the same scope as the actual LEED BD+C V4 exam. In these practice tests and in the actual LEED BD+C V4 exam, make sure you read all the questions and choices very carefully. If a question seems to have more than one answer, make sure you thoroughly understand the question and pay special attention to the wording. If still more than one answer choice seems to be the correct answer, choose the answer that best reflects the question. Regardless of how well you know the exam content, if you don't read the content very carefully, the actual LEED BD+C V4 exam can easily trick you into selecting the wrong answer.

 120 minutes

1) A LEED AP of an office-building project, working on the Access to Quality Transit credit, creates a table to evaluate the number of trips for different transit types. The project contains a bus station, a ferry terminal, and a light rail station within a half-mile (800-meter) walking distance of a functional entry. Which of the following statements would be true if none of the eligible transit types is providing weekend trips?
   a) The project cannot earn the credit.
   b) The project can earn points if the total number of bus, ferry, and light rail trips exceed the threshold set forth in the credit.
   c) The project can earn points if the total number of ferry and light rail trips exceed the threshold set forth in the credit.
   d) The project can earn points only if the number of ferry trips exceed the threshold set forth in the credit.

2) Which of the following prerequisites/credits does not refer to the US Department of Energy's Commercial Buildings Energy Consumption Survey (CBECS) database for estimating the total building energy cost?
   a) Advanced Energy Metering
   b) Building-Level Energy Metering
   c) Renewable Energy Production
   d) Green Power and Carbon Offsets

3) A LEED AP suggests that the project team implement a strategy to earn an innovation point under the Option 1: Innovation part of the Innovation credit. Which of the following strategies would work?
   a) Placing screens inside the building to educate occupants and visitors about the positive effects that green buildings have on the environment
   b) Generating all the project's energy demand by renewable energy sources
   c) Using no refrigerants at all
   d) Restoring 80% of the previously developed site

4) Project teams are encouraged to review the ANSI Consensus National Standard Guide 2.0 for Design and Construction of Sustainable Buildings and Communities for which of the following prerequisites/credits? (Choose two.)
   a) Integrative Process credit
   b) Fundamental Commissioning and Verification prerequisite
   c) Integrative Project Planning and Design prerequisite
   d) Enhanced Commissioning credit

5) Which of the following statements is false about the LT credit LEED for Neighborhood Development Location?

a) It is the credit that contains the most points in the Location and Transportation category.

b) Projects pursuing this credit will not be eligible to receive any points from the other LT credits.

c) It is not applicable to all the LEED BD+C rating systems.

d) A LEED BD+C project located inside a LEED v4—LEED for Neighborhood Development Certified Plan is eligible to receive points under this credit.

6) Which of the following credits address lighting controls? (Choose two.)

a) Integrative Process

b) Interior Lighting

c) Optimize Energy Performance

d) Light Pollution Reduction

7) Which of the following credits refers to the US Endangered Species Act?

a) Sensitive Land Protection

b) High-Priority Site

c) LEED for Neighborhood Development Location

d) Site Development—Protect or Restore Habitat

8) The project team of a retail construction project is working on the MR prerequisite Storage and Collection of Recyclables. The project team has identified the top recyclable waste streams for the project. At a minimum, for how many of the identified waste streams should the project team provide dedicated areas for separation, collection, and storage?

a) Three

b) Four

c) Five

d) Six

9) A LEED AP suggests implementing a "simple box" energy modeling analysis. Under which of the following prerequisites/credits is this required?

a) Fundamental Commissioning and Verification prerequisite

b) Enhanced Commissioning credit

c) Integrative Process credit

d) Integrative Project Planning and Design prerequisite

10) Which of the following Environmental Site Assessment (ESA) types is a survey to identify potential or existing site contamination, which generally includes reviewing the historical records and a site visit for visually identifying any sign of contamination?
   a) Phase I
   b) Phase II
   c) Scope III
   d) Phase III

11) Which of the following strategies of the EQ credit Enhanced Indoor Air Quality Strategies refers to the National Ambient Air Quality Standards?
   a) Exterior contamination prevention
   b) Increased ventilation
   c) Interior cross-contamination prevention
   d) Filtration

12) Which of the following statements is false about the Environmental Tobacco Smoke Control prerequisite?
   a) If the requirement to prohibit smoking within 25 feet (7.5 meters) cannot be implemented because of any code or regulation, project teams should provide documentation.
   b) Signage must be posted within 10 feet (3 meters) of all building entrances, and it should indicate the no-smoking policy.
   c) Only residential projects can allow smoking inside the common areas.
   d) Smoking should be prohibited outside the property line in the spaces used for business purposes.

13) Which of the following statements is false about the PBT Source Reduction—Mercury credit?
   a) The credit requires project teams to specify and install fluorescent lamps with both low mercury content and long lamp life.
   b) Per the credit, projects can install any circular fluorescent lamps or probe start metal halide lamps.
   c) It is only applicable to LEED BD+C: Healthcare projects.
   d) Project teams should specify the use of those lamps that meet the credit criteria for increased lamp life and should specify linear and U-bend fluorescent lamps to meet the rated hours and ballast type criteria.

14) A project team is working on fulfilling the water-related requirements of the Integrative Process credit. Evaluating which of the following would contribute to the "process water demand" strategies? (Choose three.)
   a) Kitchen equipment
   b) Laundry equipment
   c) Cooling towers
   d) Municipally supplied nonpotable water
   e) On-site graywater

15) Which of the following credits refers to the Cradle to Cradle certification?
   a) Building Product Disclosure and Optimization—Environmental Product Declarations
   b) Building Product Disclosure and Optimization—Sourcing of Raw Materials
   c) Building Product Disclosure and Optimization—Material Ingredients
   d) Site Assessment

16) A project team in pursuit of the Construction and Demolition Waste Management Planning prerequisite cannot implement reuse and recycling methods. What should the LEED AP suggest?
   a) Submit a credit interpretation ruling and ask for an alternative method
   b) Avoid pursuing the prerequisite
   c) Consider waste-to-energy systems and follow the European Commission Waste Framework Directive 2008/98/EC and Waste Incineration Directive 2000/76/EC
   d) Convert all the waste to energy by following REACH Optimization standards

17) Under the Green Power and Carbon Offsets credit, green power and renewable energy certificates (RECs) should be:
   a) Green-e Climate-certified or the equivalent, and they can only be used to mitigate the effects of scope 1 electricity and natural gas use
   b) Green-e Climate-certified or the equivalent, and they can only be used to mitigate the effects of scope 2 electricity use
   c) Green-e Energy-certified or the equivalent, and they can only be used to mitigate the effects of scope 2 electricity and natural gas use
   d) Green-e Energy-certified or the equivalent, and they can only be used to mitigate the effects of scope 2 electricity use

18) Under the Option 1: Historic Building Reuse part of the MR credit Building Life-Cycle Impact Reduction, projects should reuse a historic building with a "historic" designation, or the existing building should be inside the following:
   a) A historic district
   b) An infill site
   c) A brownfield site
   d) An existing building

19) Which of the following is the term that combines all the changes, improvements, issued LEED interpretations, and modifications made to a LEED rating system?
   a) Credit interpretation ruling (CIR)
   b) LEED Interpretation
   c) Addenda
   d) Appeal

20) Which of the following project types should restrict smoking on the entire site in order to earn a LEED certification?
   a) Healthcare
   b) School
   c) Data center
   d) Retail

21) A new construction project pursuing the EA credit Renewable Energy Production is estimated to use 400,000 kWh of electricity, with a rate of $0.05 per kWh, as the only energy source. To earn the credit, what is the minimum amount of equivalent cost of renewable energy that should be generated on-site?
   a) $100
   b) $200
   c) $400
   d) $2,000

22) Which of the following statements is false regarding the Building Life-Cycle Impact Reduction credit?
a) In Option 2: Renovation of Abandoned or Blighted Buildings, salvaged materials off-site that will be installed in the building cannot be included in the credit calculations.
b) In Option 3: Building and Material Reuse, project teams can use salvaged materials off-site and count them as "surface areas reused" in the credit calculations.
c) In Option 2: Renovation of Abandoned or Blighted Buildings and in Option 3: Building and Material Reuse, window assemblies and any hazardous materials that are remediated as a part of the project should be excluded from the calculations.
d) In Option 3: Building and Material Reuse, if there is any deterioration or damage, up to 25% of the building surface area may be excluded from credit calculations.

23) Under the Low-Emitting Materials credit, which of the following is the emissions and content requirement for "interior paints and coatings applied on-site"? (Choose two.)
a) General emissions evaluation
b) Exterior applied products
c) VOC content requirement for wet-applied products
d) Additional insulation requirements

24) Which of the following prerequisites/credits is not only applicable to the LEED BD+C: School projects?
a) Site Master Plan credit
b) Environmental Site Assessment prerequisite
c) Joint Use of Facilities credit
d) Minimum Acoustic Performance prerequisite

25) A project team pursuing the Option 1: No Refrigerants or Low-Impact Refrigerants part of the Enhanced Refrigerant Management credit is comparing refrigerant alternatives to be used for the cooling equipment that will be installed in the project. Below are the refrigerants' ozone depletion potentials (ODP) and global warming potentials (GWP). Which of the following refrigerants can satisfy the credit's requirements?
Refrigerant #1: 80 ODP, 0 GWP   Refrigerant #3: 0 ODP, 48 GWP
Refrigerant #2: 15 ODP, 74 GWP   Refrigerant #4: 0 ODP, 5 GWP

a) Refrigerants #1,2,3,4
b) Refrigerants #1,2,3
c) Refrigerants #3 and #4
d) Only refrigerant #4

26) "To reduce the environmental and economic harms associated with fossil fuel energy by increasing the use of self-supply of renewable energy" is the intent of which of the following?
 a) The Green Power and Carbon Offsets credit
 b) The Renewable Energy Production credit
 c) The Enhanced Refrigerant Management credit
 d) The Fundamental Refrigerant Management prerequisite

27) Some credits in the LT category require calculations of total vehicle parking capacity, such as the Reduced Parking Footprint credit or the Green Vehicles credit. Which of the following should not be included in the project's total parking capacity?
 a) New surface parking spaces
 b) Existing multilevel parking spaces
 c) Parking spaces assigned to fleet and inventory vehicles
 d) Any off-street parking spaces both inside and outside of the project boundary that serve the building users

28) Which of the following is not a "diverse use" category?
 a) Community anchor uses
 b) Community-serving retail
 c) Educational institutions
 d) Civic and community facilities

29) Which of the following is not a source of biofuel, according to LEED requirements?
 a) Untreated wood waste
 b) Landfill gas
 c) Hide products
 d) Agricultural crops or waste

30) Per the Fundamental Refrigerant Management prerequisite, projects should not use:
 a) Halon-based refrigerants
 b) Hydrochlorofluorocarbon-based refrigerants
 c) Chlorofluorocarbon-based refrigerants
 d) Hydrocarbon-based refrigerants

31) Which of the following statements is false about the Green Power and Carbon Offsets credit?
    a) Renewable energy certificates (RECs) can be purchased to mitigate the effects of the project's natural gas usage.
    b) Carbon offsets can be purchased in order to mitigate the effects of the project's electricity usage.
    c) Credit calculations are based on energy usage, not energy cost.
    d) Carbon offsets may be used to mitigate scope 1 or scope 2 emissions.

32) A new construction project is in pursuit of the Option 1: Whole-Building Energy Simulation part of the EA prerequisite Minimum Energy Performance. The project team is going to calculate the baseline building performance with a simulation. According to which of the following standards should the project team calculate the baseline building performance?
    a) ANSI/ASHRAE /IESNA Standard 90.1-2010, Appendix G, with errata
    b) ASHRAE 50% Advanced Energy Design Guide
    c) ANSI/ASHRAE/IESNA Standard 90.1-2010, with errata
    d) ANSI/ASHRAE/IESNA Standard 90.1-2010, Appendixes B and D

33) In the Reduced Parking Footprint credit, projects that have not earned points under Surrounding Density and Diverse Uses or Access to Quality Transit credits should achieve a _____ reduction from the base ratios.
    a) 10%
    b) 20%
    c) 30%
    d) 40%

34) Which of the following materials is not required to be collected and stored per the MR prerequisite Storage and Collection of Recyclables?
    a) Metals
    b) Plastics
    c) Wood
    d) Mixed paper

35) Which of the following statements is true when a demand response program is not available in the project's location?
a) The project will automatically achieve the Demand Response credit.
b) The project cannot pursue the Demand Response credit.
c) The project can achieve the Demand Response credit by providing infrastructure for future demand response programs.
d) None of the above.

36) A project team pursuing the EA credit Advanced Energy Metering is looking for ways to determine the individual end uses that use 10% or more of the building's total annual energy. If there isn't any energy model for the project, which of the following should the project team refer to in order to estimate the total building energy consumption?
a) Commercial Building Energy Consumption Survey
b) Chartered Institution of Building Services Engineers
c) Green-e
d) Energy STAR Portfolio Manager

37) A LEED AP is informing the owner of the pursuit of the Joint Use of Facilities credit. Which of the following statements would be false about that credit?
a) To earn the credit, schools can make their building space open to the general public.
b) To earn the credit, schools can contract with specific organizations to share building space.
c) The credit contains four options, and project teams can choose any one of them.
d) To earn the credit, schools can use spaces owned by other organizations that are accessible by foot.

38) A project team calculates that, in order to earn the SS credit Open Space, 10,000 square feet of open space should be provided in accordance with the project's total site area. At a minimum, how much of this space should be vegetated?
a) 1,000 square feet
b) 2,000 square feet
c) 2,500 square feet
d) 3,000 square feet

39) A LEED AP working on the Option 2: Financial Support part of the Site Development—Protect or Restore Habitat credit is searching for a land trust or conservation organization. According to that credit, within which of the following regions should the land trust or the conservation organization be located? (Choose two.)
   a) The same EPA Level II ecoregion
   b) The same EPA Level III ecoregion
   c) The project's district
   d) The project's county
   e) The project's state

40) To earn the SS credit Rainwater Management, under Option 1: Percentile of Rainfall Events, all projects (except zero-lot-line projects), should either manage the _____ percentile of regional or local rainfall events (under path 1), for 2 points, or manage the _____ percentile of regional or local rainfall events (under path 2), for 3 points.
   a) 85th, 95th
   b) 85th, 98th
   c) 95th, 98th
   d) 95th, 100th

41) For both the Fundamental Commissioning and Verification prerequisite and the Enhanced Commissioning credit, at least how many similar projects should the qualified commissioning authority have completed?
   a) One
   b) Two
   c) Three
   d) Four

42) Which of the following statements is false about the WE prerequisite Indoor Water Use Reduction?
   a) In the prerequisite calculations, the baseline flow and flush rates are specified by the Energy Policy Act of 1992 (EPAct 1992).
   b) If all the installed fixtures and fittings do not exceed WaterSense maximum levels, projects can earn the prerequisite by only documenting their fixtures and applicable appliances with "product cutsheets" or "fixture schedules" and manufacturers' information.
   c) Project teams can use nonpotable water sources (such as reclaimed water, graywater, or harvested rainwater) to establish the 20% indoor water reduction.
   d) The prerequisite also has requirements for appliance and process water use.

43) Which of the following is not required to be evaluated under the Site Assessment credit?
    a) Hydrology
    b) Topography
    c) Energy loads
    d) Human health effects

44) Which of the following statements is false about the Optimize Energy Performance credit?
    a) Under Option 1: Whole-Building Energy Simulation, on-site renewable energy sources cannot be included in the building energy model.
    b) It is the credit that contains the most points.
    c) Projects pursuing Option 2: Prescriptive Compliance: ASHRAE Advanced Energy Design Guide should comply with the appropriate ASHRAE 50% Advanced Energy Design Guide.
    d) The percentage improvement in energy performance is calculated by using the energy costs.

45) Under the Building-Level Water Metering prerequisite, for a _____, the project should commit to sharing the whole-project water use data with the USGBC, beginning on the date that the project accepts LEED certification or typical occupancy, whichever comes first.
    a) One-year period
    b) Two-year period
    c) Five-year period
    d) Ten-year period

46) Per the Option 4: Whole-Building Life-Cycle Assessment part of the MR credit Building Life-Cycle Impact Reduction, project teams should conduct a life-cycle assessment of the project's structure and enclosure, which should demonstrate a minimum of 10% reduction compared with the baseline building in at least three of the six impact categories, one of which must be the following:
    a) Acidification of land and water sources
    b) Depletion of the stratospheric ozone layer
    c) Global warming potential
    d) Formation of tropospheric ozone

47) A team member of a LEED BD+C: School project is preparing documentation for the Option 2: Pedestrian Access part of the Access to Quality Transit credit. Which of the following documentation is applicable?
   a) A map showing project boundary and transit stop locations
   b) Timetables of the eligible transits
   c) A map showing the walkshed boundary
   d) Walking routes and distances to transit stop locations

48) Which of the following LEED BD+C credit categories contains the highest number of points?
   a) Location and Transportation
   b) Energy and Atmosphere
   c) Materials and Resources
   d) Indoor Environmental Quality

49) Under the credential maintenance program, LEED APs with a specialty must earn the following:
   a) 15 continuing education hours every year after earning their credential
   b) 30 continuing education hours every year after earning their credential
   c) 30 continuing education hours every two years after earning their credential
   d) 50 continuing education hours every two years after earning their credential

50) Which of the following is not a sensitive land?
   a) Floodplains
   b) Brownfield site
   c) Habitat
   d) Water bodies

51) If project teams choose to perform flush-out during the occupancy period under the Indoor Quality Assessment credit, before the occupancy, a minimum of:
   a) 3,500 cubic feet of outdoor air per square foot of gross floor area must be provided to the space.
   b) 7,500 cubic feet of outdoor air per square foot of gross floor area must be provided to the space.
   c) 14,000 cubic feet of outdoor air per square foot of gross floor area must be provided to the space.
   d) 20,000 cubic feet of outdoor air per square foot of gross floor area must be provided to the space.

52) The Innovation credit category contains a total of:
   a) 4 points
   b) 5 points
   c) 6 points
   d) 7 points

53) Which of the following statements is false about the Construction and Demolition Waste Management credit?
   a) Wood waste that is converted to fuel (biofuel) can be included in the credit calculations as a diversion.
   b) Waste-to-energy systems may be considered waste diversion if the European Commission Waste Framework Directive 2008/98/EC and Waste Incineration Directive 2000/76/EC are followed.
   c) Hazardous materials may or may not be included in the diversion calculations at the project team's discretion.
   d) Land-clearing debris should be excluded in the diversion calculations.

54) Which of the following statements is false regarding the Bicycle Facilities credit?
   a) Retail projects are required to provide a bicycle maintenance program for employees or bicycle route assistance for employees and customers.
   b) School projects should provide dedicated bicycle lanes that extend at least to the end of the school property from the school buildings without any barriers such as fences.
   c) School projects do not need to provide any shower rooms and changing facilities to the students.
   d) Healthcare projects should include patients in the bicycle storage calculations.

55) Under the Option 1: Material Ingredient Reporting part of the Building Product Disclosure and Optimization—Material Ingredients credit, projects should demonstrate the chemical inventory of the product to at least:
   a) 0.01% of its ingredients
   b) 0.1% of its ingredients
   c) 10% of its ingredients
   d) 15% of its ingredients

56) Which of the following statements is false regarding the Interior Lighting credit?
   a) The individual lighting controls provided should contain at two lighting levels (on and off).
   b) Hospitality projects are not required to provide individual lighting controls to the guest rooms under this credit.
   c) Retail projects should provide individual lighting controls to at least 90% of the individual occupant spaces in office and administrative areas.
   d) Healthcare projects should provide individual lighting controls for at least 90% of individual occupant spaces in staff areas.

57) A project team pursuing the MR credit Design for Flexibility is discussing strategies to achieve the credit. Which of the following strategies will not contribute to that credit?
   a) Providing programmed soft space, such as administration or storage space, equal to at least 5% of departmental gross area
   b) Providing shell space equal to at least 1% of departmental gross area
   c) Installing interstitial space and designing distribution zone utility systems and equipment to serve the occupied zones
   d) Designing for future vertical expansion on at least 75% of the roof

58) Implementing which of the following strategies would not make a positive contribution to the EQ credit Daylight?
   a) Installing vision glazing
   b) Using low-height partitions in open offices
   c) Locating the private offices around the building perimeter
   d) Using transparent partitions such as interior windows placed in walls or doors

59) Which of the following is addressed under the Option 2: Additional Enhanced IAQ Strategies part of the EQ credit Enhanced Indoor Air Quality Strategies?
   a) Additional source control and monitoring
   b) Entryway systems
   c) Filtration
   d) Mixed-mode design calculations

60) A project team is performing calculations for the Option 1: Non-Roof and Roof part of the SS credit Heat Island Reduction. The project contains 5,000 square feet of steep-sloped, high-reflectance roof with an initial SRI value of 98 and a three-year-aged SRI of 90, of which 500 square feet is covered by mechanical systems. How much area of this roof can be counted as a high-reflectance roof in the credit calculations?
   a) 0 square feet
   b) 4,500 square feet
   c) 5,000 square feet
   d) 5,500 square feet

61) Under the Option 2: Multi-Attribute Optimization part of the Building Product Disclosure and Optimization—Environmental Product Declarations credit:
   a) 25% (by weight) of the permanently installed products used in the project must comply with one of the credit's criteria.
   b) 50% (by weight) of the permanently installed products used in the project must comply with at least two of the credit's criteria.
   c) 50% (by cost) of the permanently installed products used in the project must comply with one of the credit's criteria.
   d) 75% (by cost) of the permanently installed products used in the project must comply with at least two of the credit's criteria.

62) An owner of a 120,000-square-foot office-building project tells the LEED AP to avoid creating an energy model for the project under the EA prerequisite Minimum Energy Performance. What should the LEED AP suggest?
   a) Suggest creating the energy model as it is the only way to achieve a LEED certification for such a project
   b) Suggest pursuing Option 2: Prescriptive Compliance—50% ASHRAE Advanced Energy Design Guide and avoid creating the energy model
   c) Suggest pursuing Option 1: Whole-Building Energy Simulation without creating an energy model
   d) Suggest pursuing Option 3: Prescriptive Compliance: Advanced Buildings Core Performance Guide

63) Which of the following can be included or excluded—at the project team's discretion—under the WE prerequisite Outdoor Water Use Reduction calculations? (Choose two.)
   a) Food gardens
   b) Hardscape
   c) Vegetated athletic playgrounds
   d) Native plants

64) Per the Fundamental Commissioning and Verification prerequisite, project teams should complete the commissioning activities for the mechanical, electrical, plumbing, and renewable energy systems and assemblies according to _____ and _____ for HVAC&R systems as related to energy, water, indoor environmental quality, and durability.
   a) ASHRAE Guideline 0-2005, ASHRAE Guideline 1.1-2007
   b) ASHRAE 52.2-2007, ASHRAE Guideline 1.1-2007
   c) ASHRAE Guideline 0-2005, NIBS Guideline 3-2012
   d) ASHRAE 62.1-2010, ASHRAE 55-2010

65)

$$\frac{\text{Area of non-roof measures}}{0.50} + \frac{\text{Area of high-reflectance roof}}{0.75} + \frac{\text{Area of vegetated roof}}{X} \geq \text{Total site paving area} + \text{Total roof area}$$

Under the Option 1: Non-roof and Roof part of the Heat Island Reduction credit, project teams should satisfy the formula above in order to earn the credit. In the formula, what does "X" represent?
   a) 0.25
   b) 0.50
   c) 0.75
   d) 0.85

66) Under the LT credit Access to Quality Transit, what is the maximum walking distance between any functional entry of the building and an existing or planned bus rapid transit stop, a light or heavy rail station, a commuter rail station, or a commuter ferry terminal?
   a) Quarter mile (400 meters)
   b) Half mile (800 meters)
   c) One mile (1,600 meters)
   d) Two miles (3,200 meters)

67) Under the Green Vehicles credit, a LEED BD+C: New Construction project may choose to designate _____ of all parking spaces as preferred parking for sole use by green vehicles. Or instead of providing preferred parking to green vehicles, projects can provide a discounted parking rate of at least _____ to green vehicles.
   a) 5%, 10%
   b) 5%, 20%
   c) 10%, 20%
   d) 20%, 30%

68) Which of the following is not a natural refrigerant?
   a) Carbon dioxide
   b) Ammonia
   c) Halon
   d) Propane

69) A project team working on a healthcare project wants to neglect the plumbing items from the credit's calculations. In which of the following credits is this possible?
   a) Building Product and Disclosure—Sourcing of Raw Materials credit
   b) PBT Source Reduction—Lead, Cadmium, and Copper credit
   c) Indoor Water Use Reduction credit
   d) Water Metering credit

70) Which of the following systems are not required to be commissioned under the EA prerequisite Fundamental Commissioning and Verification, but they may be added to the commissioning scope at the request of the owner? (Choose two.)
   a) Renewable energy systems
   b) Building envelope
   c) Mechanical
   d) Electrical
   e) Fire protection and fire alarm systems

71) What would be the full-time equivalent (FTE) value of a building that only hosts 30 full-time employees (working 8 hours a day during workdays) and 10 part-time employees (working 4 hours a day during workdays)?
   a) 35
   b) 40
   c) 240
   d) 280

72) An office building project aiming for a LEED certification wants to pursue the LT credit Bicycle Facilities. If the project is calculated to host 500 regular building occupants, how many shower rooms will be required?
a) 2
b) 3
c) 4
d) 5

73) Under the SS credit Heat Island Reduction, in order to classify building materials according to their solar emissions and reflectance, the _____ values will be used for roofing materials and _____ values will be used for nonroof materials (such as hardscape).
a) Solar reflectance index, solar reflectance
b) Solar reflectance, solar reflectance index
c) Albedo, solar reflectance
d) Solar reflectance, emissivity

74) Under the Quality Views credit, all LEED BD+C projects—except LEED BD+C: Warehouses and Distribution Centers and LEED BD+C: Healthcare—should achieve a direct line of sight to the outdoors via vision glazing for the following:
a) 25% of all individual occupied floor spaces
b) 50% of all the regularly occupied floor area
c) 75% of all the regularly occupied floor area
d) 90% of all the multioccupant spaces

75) A project team is discussing strategies to earn the SS credit Light Pollution Reduction. The LEED AP tells the lighting designer that there are two different options that can both result in achieving that credit. What are those two options? (Choose two.)
a) Calculation method
b) Glare rating method
c) Backlight-uplight-glare rating method
d) Lighting zone method

76) A LEED BD+C: New Construction project is pursuing the EQ credit Acoustic Performance. Which of the following statements is false regarding that credit?

a) If the project team needs to install sound reinforcement or masking systems, then the installed equipment must meet the credit's requirements.

b) If no sound reinforcement or masking systems are installed, the project can still earn the credit.

c) For HVAC background noise, the project should achieve the maximum background noise levels from HVAC systems per the 2011 ASHRAE Handbook, HVAC Applications, Chapter 48, Table 1; AHRI Standard 885-2008, Table 15; or a local equivalent.

d) For all the occupied spaces, the project should address HVAC background noise, sound isolation, reverberation time, and site exterior noise.

77) The Bicycle Facilities credit requires project teams to demonstrate how far a bicyclist would need to travel from the building to a particular destination such as a diverse use or public transportation station. When calculating the walking distance between the building and any destination, the project team should do the following:

a) Measure the distance by drawing a straight line radius from the building to the desired destination.

b) Use the shortest path analysis and measure the distance along infrastructure that is safe and comfortable for pedestrians (such as sidewalks and crosswalks).

c) Measure the distance by drawing a straight line radius from the building to the desired destination, if there are safe paths that allow pedestrians to travel.

d) Either measure the distance by either drawing a straight line radius from the building to the desired location or by using the shortest path analysis.

78) Which of the following credits will not qualify for an exemplary performance point?

a) Heat Island Reduction

b) Rainwater Management

c) Places of Respite

d) Water Metering

79) Under the Option 2: Envelope Commissioning part of the Enhanced Commissioning credit, LEED refers to the following:
    a) National Institute of Building Sciences (NIBS) Guideline
    b) COMNET Modeling Guidelines and Procedures
    c) Illuminating Engineering Society of North America (IESNA)
    d) US Department of Energy's Commercial Buildings Energy Consumption Survey (CBECS)

80) Under the Quality Views credit, vision glazing should provide a clear image of the exterior and should not be blocked by obstructions defined under the credit. Which of the following cannot be considered an obstruction under the credit?
    a) Added tints that distort color balance
    b) Frits
    c) Operable window blinds
    d) Fibers

81) LEED refers to the Natural Resources Conservation Service (NRCS) under which of the following prerequisites/credits? (Choose three.)
    a) Sensitive Land Protection credit
    b) Environmental Site Assessment prerequisite
    c) Site Assessment credit
    d) Integrative Process credit
    e) Site Development—Protect or Restore Habitat credit

82) Under the Option 2: Pedestrian Access part of the Access to Quality Transit credit, LEED BD+C: School project teams should demonstrate that the specified percentages of students live within a _____ walking distance (for grades 8 and below or ages 14 and below), and a _____ walking distance (for grades 9 and above or ages 15 and above) of any functional entry of the school building.
    a) ¾-mile (1,200-meter), 1 mile (1,600-meter)
    b) ¾-mile (1,200-meter), 1 ½-mile (2,400-meter)
    c) 1-mile (1,600-meter), 1 ½-mile (2,400-meter)
    d) 1-mile (1,600-meter), 2-mile (3,200-meter)

83) The LEED AP talks with the owner about the benefits of installing a rainwater harvesting system to the project. Which of the following prerequisites/credits can this decision contribute to? (Choose two.)
   a) Indoor Water Use Reduction prerequisite
   b) Rainwater Management credit
   c) Outdoor Water Use Reduction credit
   d) Indoor Water Use Reduction prerequisite

84) _____ is storing the energy generated during off-peak hours in order to use it during peak-demand hours.
   a) Demand response
   b) Load shifting
   c) Load shedding
   d) Renewable energy certificates (RECs)

85) To qualify as a biobased product under the Option 2: Leadership Extraction Practices part of the Building Product Disclosure and Optimization—Sourcing of Raw Materials credit, the product must meet the:
   a) Forest Stewardship Council (FSC) standard
   b) Sustainable Agriculture Network's Sustainable Agriculture Standard
   c) GreenScreen standard
   d) ISO 14044 standard

86) For the Daylight credit's calculations, under all the options, LEED BD+C: New Construction projects should consider the following:
   a) Regularly occupied floor area
   b) Perimeter floor area
   c) Gross floor area
   d) Site area

87) Under option 2 of the Sensitive Land Protection credit, LEED restricts development within _____ of water bodies, with the exception of some minor improvements.
   a) 50 feet (15 meters)
   b) 75 feet (22 meters)
   c) 100 feet (30 meters)
   d) 200 feet (60 meters)

88) A project designer is planning to remove some trees from the site in order to allow for a hardscape area. A LEED AP tells the designer that removing the trees may result in the denial of the SS credit Sensitive Land Protection. Removing which of the following trees would not result in denial of that credit?
   a) All the trees whose diameters are more than 6 inches (150 millimeters) at breast height
   b) Trees that are under 40% condition rating
   c) All the dead trees
   d) Trees with 80% condition rating

89) A LEED AP of a 50,000-square-foot LEED BD+C: Retail project wants to calculate the number of short-term bicycle storage spaces that should be provided to the project in order to earn the Bicycle Facilities credit. The building contains 100 peak visitors. What is the minimum number of short-term bicycle storage spaces that should be provided?
   a) 3
   b) 10
   c) 20
   d) 25

90) A project team determines that it has achieved 5 out of the 6 regional priority points for the project's location. How many bonus points can the project receive under the Regional Priority credit?
   a) Two
   b) Four
   c) Five
   d) Six

91) A project team is discussing which option to pursue under the EA prerequisite Minimum Energy Performance. Pursuing which of the following options, will result in failure to gain the Optimize Energy Performance credit?
   a) Option 1: Whole-Building Energy Simulation
   b) Option 2: Prescriptive Compliance: ASHRAE 50% Advanced Energy Design Guide
   c) Option 3: Prescriptive Compliance: Advanced Buildings™ Core Performance™ Guide
   d) Both Option 2: Prescriptive Compliance: ASHRAE 50% Advanced Energy Design Guide and Option 3: Prescriptive Compliance: Advanced Buildings™ Core Performance™ Guide

92) Per the Option 1: Lighting Control part of the Interior Lighting credit, project teams should provide individual lighting controls that enable occupants to adjust the lighting to suit their preferences for at least:
a) 50% of the individual occupant spaces
b) 80% of the individual occupant spaces
c) 90% of the individual occupant spaces
d) 100% of the individual occupant spaces

93) A project owner decides to install a permanent steel structure to carry the national flag next to the building's main entrance. The project team is in pursuit of the SS credit Light Pollution Reduction, and the owner wants the national flag to be illuminated at night. If the project is located inside an MLO3 zone, what should the LEED AP suggest about the national flag lighting?
a) Suggest nothing, as national flag lighting will already be exempt from the credit requirements
b) Suggest including this lighting under the uplight calculations to confirm its compliance
c) Suggest turning this lighting off from midnight to six in the morning for credit compliance
d) Suggest choosing a luminaire with a low backlight rating

94) For the EQ credit Construction Indoor Air Quality Management Plan, which of the following project types should develop a plan based on the British Standard (BS 5228) to reduce noise emissions and vibrations from construction equipment and other nonroad engines?
a) Schools
b) Healthcare
c) Retail
d) New construction

95) Which of the following cannot be considered a low-impact development strategy?
a) Use of dry ponds
b) Use of bioswales and vegetated filters
c) Use of materials with higher solar reflectance and solar reflectance index values
d) Bioretention

96) Which of the following cannot qualify as a bicycle network?
    a) Off-street bicycle paths or trails at least 8 feet (2.5 meters) wide for a two-way path and at least 5 feet (1.5 meters) wide for a one-way path
    b) Streets with a 40 mph (65 kmh) speed limit
    c) Physically designated on-street bicycle lanes that are at least 5 feet (1.5 meters) wide
    d) Streets that are designed for a target speed of 25 mph (40 kmh)

97) Which of the following is not directly addressed under the Building Product Disclosures and Optimization credits?
    a) Assessment of the ingredients of the materials
    b) Principles employed during the sourcing of raw materials
    c) Environmental Product Declarations
    d) VOC levels of the materials used inside the building

98) Which of the following statements is false about the SS credit Site Master Plan?
    a) The credit is only applicable to healthcare projects.
    b) In order to be eligible for this credit, projects should plan for future developments.
    c) The master plan created under the credit should include both the current construction activity and future construction activities within the building's life span.
    d) It is essential to include flexibility in the site master plan to allow for future changes in the planned developments

99) In order to pursue the Optimize Energy Performance credit under Option 1: Whole Building Energy Simulation, new construction projects should make further reductions from their baseline energy use from:
    a) 4% to 48%
    b) 5% to 50%
    c) 6% to 50%
    d) 7% to 48%

100) A project team decides to pursue pilot credits to earn more points in total. What is the maximum number of points a project team can earn for pilot credits, under Option 3: Additional Strategies of the Innovation credit?
    a) 1 point
    b) 2 points
    c) 3 points
    d) 4 points

PRACTICE TEST 3 – ANSWERS

A score above 80 would indicate well preparation for the exam.

1	A	26	B	51	A	76	D
2	B	27	C	52	C	77	B
3	A	28	C	53	C	78	D
4	A and C	29	C	54	D	79	A
5	C	30	C	55	B	80	C
6	A and B	31	A	56	A	81	A, C, and E
7	A	32	A	57	B	82	B
8	B	33	B	58	C	83	B and C
9	C	34	C	59	A	84	B
10	A	35	C	60	B	85	B
11	A	36	A	61	C	86	A
12	C	37	C	62	A	87	C
13	B	38	C	63	A and C	88	B
14	A, B, and C	39	B and E	64	A	89	C
15	C	40	C	65	C	90	B
16	C	41	B	66	B	91	C
17	D	42	C	67	B	92	C
18	A	43	C	68	C	93	A
19	C	44	A	69	A	94	B
20	B	45	C	70	B and E	95	C
21	B	46	C	71	A	96	B
22	D	47	C	72	C	97	D
23	A and C	48	B	73	A	98	A
24	B	49	C	74	C	99	C
25	C	50	B	75	A and C	100	C

SECTION 7

PRACTICE TEST 3 ANSWERS & EXPLANATIONS

1) A

Under the Access to Quality Transit credit, the qualifying transits should both meet the required total number of trips for both weekdays and weekends.

Only school projects can neglect weekend trips if the students do not commute to school on weekends. However, for this question, the project is an office-building project.

2) B

3) A

LEED encourages projects to find new and unique ways of exceeding green building principles that have not been previously covered in the LEED rating systems. If projects can create their own innovation credits, they can then receive extra points under the Option 1: Innovation part of the Innovation credit.

An example of this might be a LEED-certified building that educates occupants and visitors about the positive effects that green buildings have on the environment—possibly using screens situated in common areas.

The other choices are already addressed under other credits. Therefore, implementing those strategies would not bring a point under the Option 1: Innovation part of the Innovation credit.

4) A and C

To become familiar with the integrative process, project teams are encouraged to review the **ANSI Consensus National Standard Guide 2.0 for Design and Construction of Sustainable Buildings and Communities** both for the Integrative Project Planning and Design prerequisite and for the Integrative Process credit.

5) C

The LEED for Neighborhood Development Location credit is applicable to all LEED BD+C rating systems.

6) A and B

Under the Integrative Process credit, project teams should assess at least two strategies related to each of the following:
  - ➤ Site conditions: Evaluate shading, exterior lighting, landscaping, hardscape, and adjacent site conditions.
  - ➤ Massing and orientation: Evaluate and optimize the massing and orientation effect on sizing, energy consumption, lighting, and renewable energy opportunities. Evaluate the number of floors, building footprint, and configuration.
  - ➤ Basic envelope attributes: Evaluate the wall and roof insulation values, thermal mass, glazing characteristics, window-to-wall ratios, shading, and window operability.
  - ➤ Lighting levels: Evaluate interior surface reflectance values, lighting needs and levels in the occupied spaces, daylighting, high-efficiency lighting fixtures, and **lighting controls**.
  - ➤ Thermal comfort ranges: Evaluate thermal comfort range options and thermal comfort parameters.
  - ➤ Plug and process load needs: Evaluate reducing plug and process loads through programmatic solutions, such as equipment and purchasing policies, layout options, and more.
  - ➤ Programmatic and operational parameters: Evaluate multifunctioning spaces, space allotment per person, operating schedules, reduction of building area, and anticipated operations and maintenance.

Also, the Interior Lighting credit addresses lighting controls under Option 1: Lighting Control.

7) A

Under option 2 of the Sensitive Land Protection credit, no development can be made inside land identified as "habitat." And for land to be identified as "habitat," it should meet one of the following criteria:

- It should contain species listed as threatened or endangered under the **US Endangered Species Act** or the state's endangered species act.
- It should contain species or ecological communities identified by NatureServe as GH (possibly extinct), G1 (critically imperiled), or G2 (imperiled). For international projects, a local equivalent—such as the International Union of Conservation of Nature Red List or something similar—should be documented.
- For projects outside the United States, the land should contain threatened or endangered species under the local equivalent code standards that are not covered by the NatureServe data.

8) B

Retail projects should conduct a waste stream analysis and identify a project's top five recyclable waste streams (by weight or volume) using consistent metrics throughout.

And once the waste stream study is completed, project teams should list the top **four** recyclable waste streams and provide dedicated areas for separation, collection, and storage of the recyclables, which should also be accessible to waste haulers and building occupants.

9) C

Under the Integrative Process credit, before completing the schematic design, project teams should perform a "simple box" energy modeling analysis that will enable the project teams to see the approximate energy usage of the building and evaluate strategies on how to reduce energy use by questioning default assumptions. A simple box energy modeling analysis uses a preliminary building model to analyze the building's energy loads. Project teams can use the EPA's Target Finder tool or a similar tool in order to benchmark energy performance. Target Finder allows projects to set target goals for a building design's energy demands. And with the enhancements in the design, project teams can see the savings in energy demand.

10) A

A **Phase I** Environmental Site Assessment (ESA) is a survey to identify potential or existing site contamination, and it generally includes reviewing the historical records, a site visit for visually identifying any sign of contamination, and a narrative that indicates whether a Phase II ESA is required.

A Phase II ESA covers the testing of the on-site soil, groundwater, and more, and it determines how much contamination exists on-site.

A Phase III ESA is the first step for the remediation process, and it covers the evaluation of the remediation options and costs.

11) A

Under the exterior contamination prevention strategy of the Enhanced Air Quality Strategies credit, the project team should design the building to minimize and control the entry of pollutants into the building. Through computational fluid dynamics modeling, Gaussian dispersion analyses, wind tunnel modeling, or tracer gas modeling, the project team should ensure that the outdoor air contaminant concentrations at the outdoor air intakes are following the requirements listed in the following table:

Pollutants	Maximum concentration	Referenced Standard
The pollutants regulated by National Ambient Air Quality Standards	Allowable annual average OR 8- or 24-hour average where an annual standard does not exist OR Rolling 3-month average	National Ambient Air Quality Standards

In order to fulfill this strategy, the outdoor air intakes should be located away from the sources of pollutants. Next, the project teams should select one of the modeling tools listed above and model the contaminant travel at worst-case meteorological conditions. The model should be conducted according to the National Ambient Air Quality Standards and should confirm that the concentrations of the pollutants regulated by the National Ambient Air Quality Standards are below the threshold values.

12) C

All the LEED BD+C projects should prohibit smoking inside all common areas. Residential projects have the option to allow smoking inside the residential units by pursuing Option 2: Compartmentalization of Smoking Areas. In this option, each unit must be compartmentalized to prevent excessive leakage between units. Plus, the following would apply:

➤ All exterior doors and operable windows in the residential units should be weather-stripped to minimize leakage from outdoors.

➤ All doors leading from residential units into common hallways should be weather-stripped.

➤ By sealing penetrations in the walls, ceilings, and floors and by sealing vertical chases, the project team should minimize uncontrolled pathways for the transfer of smoke and other indoor air pollutants between residential units.

➤ The project team should demonstrate a maximum leakage of 0.23 cubic feet per minute per square foot at 50 Pa of enclosure. This would include surfaces enclosing the apartment, exterior and party walls, floors, ceilings, or any similar surfaces.

13) B

Per the PBT Source Reduction—Mercury credit, projects **cannot** install any circular fluorescent lamps or probe start metal halide lamps.

14) A,B, and C

Evaluating on-site graywater and municipally supplied nonpotable water would contribute to the "supply sources" strategies. Evaluating kitchen equipment, laundry equipment, and cooling towers would contribute to the "process water demand" strategies.

Under the water-related requirements of the Integrative Process credit, project teams should evaluate all of the following:

➤ Indoor water demand: Evaluate the design demand volumes of the flow and flush fixtures in accordance with the Indoor Water Use Reduction prerequisite.

➤ Outdoor water demand: Evaluate landscape irrigation demand volume in accordance with the Outdoor Water Use Reduction prerequisite.

➤ Process water demand: Evaluate the **cooling tower, kitchen and laundry equipment**, and other equipment-process, water-demand volumes, as applicable.

➤ Supply sources: Evaluate all the potential nonpotable water sources that can be used to reduce potable water usage such as on-site rainwater graywater, municipally supplied nonpotable water, HVAC equipment condensate, and more.

15) C

Building Product Disclosure and Optimization—Material Ingredients refers to the Cradle to Cradle (C_2C) certification. Cradle to Cradle Certification involves assessment of the ingredients of a product for environmental and human health hazards and awards Basic-, Bronze-, Silver-, Gold-, or Platinum-level Cradle to Cradle Certification to the products with preferable life-cycle impacts. And since the mentioned credit is about analyzing the ingredients of a product, Cradle to Cradle Certification serves as a great tool.

16) C

Under the Construction and Demolition Waste Management Planning prerequisite, projects that cannot implement reuse and recycling methods can consider waste-to-energy systems if the European Commission Waste Framework Directive 2008/98/EC and Waste Incineration Directive 2000/76/EC are followed. Waste-to-energy facilities must meet the applicable European Committee for Standardization (CEN) EN 303 standards.

As the solution is already defined under the prerequisite, submitting a credit interpretation ruling will not help the project team.

If the project team avoids pursuing the prerequisite, the LEED certification will not be awarded.

At last, REACH Optimization is European Union legislation that requires all chemicals sold to be evaluated based on their hazard profiles, and it is referred to under the Building Product Disclosure and Optimization—Material Ingredients credit.

17) D

18) A

19) C

"**Addenda**" is the term that combines all the changes, improvements, issued LEED interpretations, and modifications made to a LEED rating system. Just as a piece of software updates itself once a week or so to incorporate the latest updates, LEED rating systems are updated with addenda.

After LEED v4 was released, addenda have been continuously issued at the USGBC's website, which combines all the updates made to that rating system through LEED interpretations, modifications, and improvements. In addition, a project that registers with LEED Online after any issued addenda will be automatically subject to the addenda's requirements.

20) B

21) B

Under the Renewable Energy Production credit, projects should use renewable energy systems to offset building energy costs.

The percentage of renewable energy should be calculated with the following equation:

$$\text{\% renewable energy generated} = \frac{\text{Equivalent cost of usable energy produced by the renewable energy system}}{\text{Total building annual energy cost}}$$

Since the project is estimated to use 400,000 kWh of electricity, with a rate of $0.05 per kWh, as the only energy source, the building's total annual energy cost can be calculated as follows:

Building's total annual energy cost = 400,000 x 0.05 = $20,000

In the credit, points are awarded according to the project's percentage of renewable energy use, as shown in the following table:

Percentage of renewable energy	Points (except Core and Shell)	Points (Core and Shell)
1%	1	1
3%	—	2
5%	2	3
10%	3	—

Since 1% is the minimum amount of energy that should be generated using the renewable energy sources, the new construction project will need to generate electricity with an equivalent cost of:

$$\$20,000 \times 0.01 = \mathbf{\$200}$$

22) D

Since Option 2: Renovation of Abandoned or Blighted Buildings (not option 3) is for abandoned or blighted buildings, the option allows project teams to demolish any damaged or deteriorated parts of the building, up to 25% of the building's surface area, and exclude them from the credit calculations. However, that is not the case for Option 3: Building and Material Reuse. In option 3, project teams can only exclude the removed hazardous materials from the credit calculations. And the calculations should include any removed surface area (if nonhazardous), even if it was removed because of damage or deterioration.

In option 2, salvaged materials off-site that will be installed in the building cannot be included in the credit calculations though that option is more about keeping and reusing the existing building materials as much as possible. However, in option 3, project teams can use salvaged materials off-site and count them as "surface areas reused" in the credit calculations.

It is also important to note that in both option 2 and option 3, window assemblies and any hazardous materials that are remediated as a part of the project should be excluded from the calculations.

23) A and C

24) B

The Environmental Site Assessment prerequisite is also applicable to healthcare projects. See Appendix C — Prerequisites/Credits and Their Applicable Rating Systems.

25) C

Under the Option 1: No Refrigerants or Low-Impact Refrigerants part of the Enhanced Refrigerant Management credit, projects should not use any refrigerants or only use naturally occurring or synthetic refrigerants that have an ODP of **0** and a GWP of less than **50**. Therefore, refrigerants #3 and #4 can both satisfy the credit.

26) B

"To encourage the reduction of greenhouse gas emissions through the use of grid-source, renewable energy technologies, and carbon mitigation projects" is the intent of the Green Power and Carbon Offsets credit.

"To reduce ozone depletion and support early compliance with the Montreal Protocol while minimizing direct contributions to climate change" is the intent of the Enhanced Refrigerant Management credit.

"Reduce ozone depletion" is the intent of the Fundamental Refrigerant Management prerequisite.

27) C

For the parking capacity calculations, the following parking spaces must be included in total parking capacity:
- New and existing surface parking spaces
- New and existing garage or multilevel parking spaces
- Any off-street parking spaces both inside and outside of the project boundary that serve the building users

The following parking spaces should not be included in total parking capacity:
- Public on-street parking spaces
- **Parking spaces assigned to fleet and inventory vehicles (unless these vehicles are used by employees for commuting as well as business purposes)**
- Motorbike or bicycle spaces

If there are shared parking spaces among two or more buildings (which is also called pooled parking), then the project's share in the parking spaces should be included in the calculations.

Note that if there isn't any parking area assigned to the project, the project will be awarded the Reduced Parking Footprint credit; however, such a situation would not merit the award of the Green Vehicles credit.

28) C

Diverse uses are grouped under five categories: "food retail," "community-serving retail," "services," "civic and community facilities," and "community anchor uses."

29) C

Biofuels are fuels produced from organic material. Biofuel includes untreated wood waste, landfill gas, agricultural crops or waste, animal waste, and other types of organic waste.

On the other hand, biobased materials are products other than food that are biological products, renewable agricultural materials, or forestry materials. Biobased materials are derived from biomass. Plants and animals can be an example of biobased materials. However, hide products, such as leather and other animal skin material, are excluded in LEED calculations.

30) C

31) A

Under this credit, RECs can <u>only</u> be used to mitigate the effects of scope 2 electricity use (not natural gas). However, carbon offsets may be used to mitigate scope 1 or scope 2 emissions on a metric ton of carbon dioxide-equivalent basis, and they can be used for nonelectricity energy sources, such as natural gas, as well as electricity sources.

Also, under this credit, projects should determine the percentage of green power or carbon offsets based on the quantity of energy consumed. Note that calculating the energy based on energy quantity is not the case for some other LEED prerequisites/credits like the Renewable Energy Production credit or the Minimum Energy Performance prerequisite since they require energy calculations based on energy costs, not quantities.

32) A

On the exam, expect to see some questions with very similar answer choices, as is the case for the question above.

Under the Option 1: Whole-Building Energy Simulation part of the Minimum Energy Performance Project prerequisite, project teams should calculate the baseline building performance according to **ANSI/ASHRAE /IESNA Standard 90.1-2010, Appendix G, with errata**. In addition to the energy modeling requirements, project designs should meet the mandatory provisions of ANSI/ASHRAE/IESNA Standard 90.1-2010, with errata.

ASHRAE 50% Advanced Energy Design Guide is referred to under option 2 of the Minimum Energy Performance prerequisite, and it is not addressed under option 1.

And under this prerequisite, teams for projects outside the United States will refer to ANSI/ASHRAE/IESNA Standard 90.1-2010, Appendixes B and D and determine the appropriate climate zone for their project.

33) B

Below are the two cases under the credit:

Case 1: Baseline location
Projects that have not earned points under Surrounding Density and Diverse Uses or Access to Quality Transit credits should achieve a **20%** reduction from the base ratios.

Case 2: Dense and/or transit-served location
Projects that have earned 1 or more points under either the Surrounding Density and Diverse Uses credit or the Access to Quality Transit credit should achieve a 40% reduction from the base ratios.

In other words, if the project is in a dense and/or transit-served location, the project should further decrease its parking capacity from the base ratios of the Parking Consultants Council.

34) C

Under the Storage and Collection of Recyclables prerequisite, recyclable materials must include mixed paper, corrugated cardboard, glass, plastics, and metals (not wood). And projects should provide dedicated areas that can be accessible by waste haulers and building occupants for the collection and storage of recyclable materials for the entire building. Collection and storage areas can be located separately as well.

35) C

Projects can achieve the Demand Response credit by providing infrastructure for future demand response programs when a demand response program is not available in the project's location, under Case 2: Demand Response Program Not Available.

36) A

If option 1 of the Minimum Energy Performance prerequisite was pursued—which requires the calculation of the total building energy cost with an energy simulation—projects could use that simulation to determine individual end uses representing 10% or more of the building's total annual energy.

But for this case, since there isn't any energy model created for the project, the project team can use the **US Department of Energy's Commercial Buildings Energy Consumption Survey (CBECS)** database to estimate the total building energy cost. In LEED, CBECS is used in lots of credits (such as the Renewable Energy Production credit and the Green Power and Carbon Offsets credit) to estimate total building energy consumption.

LEED refers to the Chartered Institution of Building Services Engineers (CIBSE) for ventilation strategies under the Minimum Indoor Air Quality Performance prerequisite and Indoor Air Quality Strategies credit.

Green-e is the leading certification program for green power generation in the United States.

On the other hand, the ENERGY STAR Portfolio Manager is an interactive, online management tool that enables the tracking and assessment of energy and water consumption. It was set up by the EPA as a part of the ENERGY STAR program.

37) C

The Joint Use of Facilities credit contains **three options** (not four), which are as follows:

Option 1: Make Building Space Open to the General Public
Option 2: Contract with Specific Organizations to Share Building Space
Option 3: Use Shared Space Owned by Other Organizations

38) C

Under the Open Space credit, a minimum of 25% of the provided outdoor space must be vegetated (turf grass does not count as vegetation) or should have an overhead vegetated canopy. For this question, the required vegetated space would be:

10,000 x 0.25 = **2,500 square feet**

39) B and E

Under the Option 2: Financial Support part of the Site Development—Protect or Restore Habitat credit, the financial support must be provided to a land trust or conservation organization within the same **EPA Level III ecoregion** or the **project's state**.

40) C

Under the Option 1: Percentile of Rainfall Events part of the Rainwater Management credit, all projects except zero-lot-line projects should either manage the **95th percentile** of regional or local rainfall events (under path 1), for 2 points, or manage the **98th percentile** of regional or local rainfall events (under path 2), for 3 points.

Only for zero-lot-line projects in urban areas with a minimum density of a 1.5 floor-to-area ratio, project teams should manage the runoff from the developed site for the 85th percentile of regional or local rainfall events, by using low-impact development and green infrastructure to best replicate the natural site hydrology. (Zero-lot-line projects are the projects in which the project boundary exactly aligns with the building footprint. In other words, the building sits on the whole project site.)

41) B

For both the Fundamental Commissioning and Verification prerequisite and the Enhanced Commissioning credit, the qualified CxA should have completed commissioning for **at least two** similar projects from the early design phase to a minimum of ten months of occupancy.

42) C

One important thing to note under the Indoor Water Use Reduction prerequisite is that project teams cannot use nonpotable water sources (such as reclaimed water, graywater, or harvested rainwater) to establish the 20% indoor water reduction. However, this can happen under the Indoor Water Use Reduction credit. (This rule is similar to the Outdoor Water Use Reduction prerequisite and credit since nonpotable water sources cannot be used under the Outdoor Water Use Reduction prerequisite calculations, but they can be used for the Outdoor Water Use Reduction credit calculations).

If all the installed fixtures and fittings do not exceed WaterSense maximum levels, projects can earn the prerequisite by only documenting their fixtures and applicable appliances with "product cutsheets" or "fixture schedules" and manufacturers' information. This time there will be no need to calculate the indoor water consumption of the building if the project team does not intend to pursue the credit of this prerequisite: the Indoor Water Use Reduction credit. The credit awards a point for further reduction of indoor water consumption, but to calculate the established percent of water reduction, project team needs to calculate the indoor water consumption in this prerequisite. Using solely WaterSense-labeled products will not be sufficient to determine the exact percentage reduction, which is also important to know for exam purposes.

Also, in the Indoor Water Use Reduction prerequisite, all the installed appliances and processes must meet the following standards:

Appliance	Requirement
Residential clothes washer	ENERGY STAR or performance equivalent
Commercial clothes washer	CEE Tier 3A
Residential dishwasher	ENERGY STAR or performance equivalent
Pre-rinse spray valves	Less than 1.3 gpm (4.9 lpm)
Ice machine	ENERGY STAR or performance equivalent that uses air-cooled or closed-loop cooling

Projects outside the United States can use appliances without the ENERGY STAR label, but project teams should still ensure that they meet ENERGY STAR specifications available on the ENERGY STAR website.

Process	Requirement
Heat rejection and cooling	No once-through cooling with potable water for any equipment or appliances that reject heat
Cooling towers and evaporative coolers	Must contain makeup water meters, conductivity controllers, overflow alarms, and efficient drift eliminators

43) C

A site assessment includes evaluation of topography, hydrology, climate, vegetation, soils, human use, and human health effects.

44) A

Unlike in the Minimum Energy Performance prerequisite, under the Optimize Energy Performance credit's Option 1: Whole Building Energy Simulation, projects using on-site renewable energy sources can count the on-site renewable energy generated in the credit calculations. Project teams should calculate the total amount of renewable energy generated and then convert this value to the equivalent cost of energy. Next, in the credit calculations they can either include this energy in the building energy model, or they can directly subtract this number from the building's total annual energy cost and recalculate their percentage of annual energy cost savings.

45) C

46) C
Under the Option 4: Whole-Building Life-Cycle Assessment part of the Building Life-Cycle Impact Reduction credit, for new construction (buildings or portions of buildings), project teams should conduct a life-cycle assessment of the project's structure and enclosure, which should demonstrate a minimum of 10% reduction compared with the baseline building in at least three of the six following impact categories, one of which must be **global warming potential**:

- Global warming potential (greenhouse gases)
- Depletion of the stratospheric ozone layer
- Acidification of land and water sources
- Eutrophication
- Formation of tropospheric ozone
- Depletion of nonrenewable energy resources

47) C
Such projects should provide a map showing the walkshed boundary. Documentation for the rest of the choices is applicable to the school projects pursuing Option 1: Transit-Served Location.

A map showing the walkshed boundary is required to demonstrate that the specified percentages of students live within a three-quarter-mile (1,200-meter) walking distance (for grades 8 and below or ages 14 and below), and a 1 1/2-mile (2,400-meter) walking distance (for grades 9 and above or ages 15 and above) of any functional entry of the school building.

48) B
The following are the credit categories for the LEED BD+C rating system and their point values:

- Integrative Process (1 point)
- Location and Transportation (16 points)
- Sustainable Sites (10 points)
- Water Efficiency (11 points)
- Energy and Atmosphere (33 points) (Category containing the highest points!)
- Materials and Resources (13 points)
- Indoor Environmental Quality (16 points)
- Innovation (6 points)
- Regional Priority (4 points)

49) C

50) B

Sensitive lands are ecologically sensitive areas such as <u>prime farmlands</u>, <u>floodplains</u>, <u>habitat</u>, <u>water bodies</u>, or <u>wetland</u>.

A brownfield site is a previously developed site that was contaminated with waste or pollution and is not considered a sensitive land. A site that is left from an abandoned building in which the contamination is not yet known can also be classified as a brownfield site.

51) A

If the project teams choose to conduct the flush-out during the occupancy period, Path 2: During Occupancy under Option 1: Flush-Out should be chosen. Under this path, before the occupancy, a minimum of **3,500 cubic feet of outdoor air per square foot of gross floor area must be provided to the space** while maintaining an internal temperature between 60° F and 80° F (15° C–27° C), and relative humidity should be no higher than 60%.

This flush-out process should continue until a total of 14,000 cubic feet of outdoor air per square foot of gross floor area is delivered to the space. In other words, if the project teams provide 3,500 cubic feet of outdoor air per square foot of gross floor area during the preoccupancy flush-out, the teams will need to provide the remaining 10,500 cubic feet of outdoor air per square foot of gross floor area during the postoccupancy period.

52) C

The Innovation credit contains 5 points, and the Innovation credit category contains 6 points with the LEED Accredited Professional credit.

53) C

Excavated soil, land-clearing debris, alternative daily cover (ADC), and hazardous materials should <u>always be excluded</u> in LEED diversion calculations.

54) D

LEED BD+C: Healthcare projects should **exclude** patients from their bicycle storage and shower-room calculations.

55) B

Under the Option 1: Material Ingredient Reporting part of the Building Product Disclosure and Optimization—Material Ingredients credit, project teams should use at least 20 different permanently installed building products from at least five different manufacturers that use the required programs to demonstrate the chemical inventory of the product to at least **0.1%**

(1,000 parts per million) of its ingredients.

56) A

Under this credit, the individual lighting should contain **at least three lighting levels** (on, off, midlevel), and the midlevel should be between 30% and 70% of the maximum illumination level (daylight contributions are not included).

57) B

Under the Design for Flexibility credit, project teams should provide shell space equal to **at least 5% of departmental gross area**, not 1%. Shell space is the type of space that is designed to be used in future expansion. It is space that is typically left unfinished. Projects should locate the shell spaces so that they can be occupied without displacing occupied space.

58) C

Locating the private offices around the building perimeter would block the daylight. Rather, private offices should be located closer to the core of the building to allow daylight to enter.

59) A

Below are the strategies under the Option 2: Additional Enhanced IAQ Strategies part of the Enhanced Indoor Air Quality Strategies credit:
- Exterior contamination prevention
- Increased ventilation
- Carbon dioxide monitoring
- Additional source control and monitoring
- Natural ventilation room-by-room calculations

60) B

For this question, the SRI and three-year-aged SRI value of the high-reflectance roof meet the credit's requirements. However, roof areas covered by mechanical equipment are always excluded in the calculations.

Since 500 square feet of the high-reflectance roof is covered by mechanical systems, the applicable roof area that should be used in the credit's calculations would be as follows:

Applicable high-reflectance roof area: 5,000 − 500 = **4,500 square feet**

61) C

Under the Option 2: Multi-Attribute Optimization part of the Building Product Disclosure and

Optimization—Environmental Product Declarations credit, **50% (by cost) of the permanently installed products used in the project must comply with one of the following criteria:**

- ➤ Third-party-certified products that demonstrate impact reduction below the industry average in at least three of the following five impact categories are valued at 100% of their cost for credit-achievement calculations.

  - Global warming potential (greenhouse gases)
  - Depletion of the stratospheric ozone layer
  - Acidification of land and water sources
  - Eutrophication
  - Formation of tropospheric ozone and depletion of nonrenewable energy resources

- ➤ Other USGBC-approved programs—This category includes products that comply with other USGBC-approved multi-attribute frameworks.

62) A

A 120,000-square-foot office project can only pursue Option 1: Whole-Building Energy Simulation. And since we are talking about a prerequisite, creating the energy model is the project's only choice in order to achieve LEED certification.

In order to choose which option to pursue under the Minimum Energy Performance prerequisite, the project must comply with the project size and type requirements of the selected option.

All project teams can pursue option 1 of this prerequisite as long as they create an energy model and comply with the prerequisite's requirements. However, to pursue option 2 and option 3, projects should meet their eligibility requirements.

Option 2 is for projects that basically do not contain unique designs and systems beyond simple improvements to the MEP systems. Office buildings less than 100,000 square feet (9,290 square meters), retail buildings between 20,000 and 100,000 square feet (1,860–9,290 square meters), school buildings of any size, and hospitals larger than 100,000 square feet (9,290 square meters) are eligible to pursue this option. In other words, **the 120,000-square-foot project mentioned in the question cannot pursue option 2.**

In order to pursue option 3 of this prerequisite, projects should be less than 100,000 square feet (9,290 square meters), and the project should not be a school, healthcare facility, warehouse, or laboratory. **Again, the 120,000-square-foot project mentioned in the question would not be able to pursue this option.**

63) A and C

Under the Outdoor Water Use Reduction prerequisite, nonvegetated surfaces (such as pavements) must be excluded from landscape-area calculations. Athletic fields and playgrounds, if vegetated, and food gardens may be included or excluded in the prerequisite calculations at the project team's discretion.

64) A

See Appendix A — Summary of ASHRAE Standards.

65) C

66) B

Under the Access to Quality Transit credit, projects should locate any functional entry of the building within a quarter-mile (400-meter) walking distance of existing or planned bus, streetcar, or rideshare stops. Or any functional entry of the building must be located within a **half-mile (800-meter)** walking distance of existing or planned bus rapid transit stops, light or heavy rail stations, commuter rail stations, or commuter ferry terminals.

67) B

Under the Green Vehicles credit, LEED BD+C: New Construction and Renovation projects should designate **5%** of all parking spaces as preferred parking for sole use by green vehicles. Preferred parking spaces should be distributed proportionally among various parking sections, if they exist, including short-term, long-term, customer, and visitor parking sections. Required signage should be posted on the preferred parking locations, and that signage should clearly show that those preferred locations are reserved for green vehicles.

Or instead of providing preferred parking to green vehicles, projects can provide a discounted parking rate of at least **20%** to green vehicles. The discounted rate must be publicly posted at the entrance of the parking area and should be available to every green vehicle permanently.

68) C

Carbon dioxide (CO_2), ammonia (NH_3), and propane are all natural refrigerants. Halons are chemicals that contribute to ozone depletion and are used in fire suppression systems.

69) A

For all the three BPDO credits (including BPDO—Sourcing of Raw Materials), mechanical, electrical, plumbing, and furniture items are not considered permanently installed building products and are typically excluded from the credit calculations. However, if the project team considers them "permanently installed building products," they can be included in the credit calculations as long as they are also included in other BPDO credits.

The Water Metering, PBT Source Reduction—Lead, Cadmium, and Copper, and Indoor Water Use Reduction credits are heavily linked to plumbing items.

70) B and E

Under the Fundamental Commissioning and Verification prerequisite, systems that will be a part of the fundamental commissioning process are as follows:

- Mechanical, including HVAC&R (heating, ventilating, air-conditioning and refrigeration)
- Plumbing (including domestic hot water systems, pumps, and controls)
- Electrical (including service, distribution, lighting, and controls, including daylighting controls)
- Renewable energy systems

Systems that are not required to be commissioned under this prerequisite but may be added to the Cx scope at the request of the owner include the following:

- Building envelope
- Life safety systems
- Communications and data systems
- Fire protection and fire alarm systems
- Process equipment

71) A

The number of FTE occupants is based on a standard 8-hour occupancy period. A full-time staff member who works 8 hours a day will have an FTE of 1, and a part-time staff member who works 4 hours a day will have an FTE of 0.5. FTE calculations also include multiple shifts.

In a building that contains 30 full-time occupants (working 8 hours a day during workdays) and 10 part-time occupants (working 4 hours a day during workdays), the total FTE for the full-time and part-time staff would be:

$$(30x1) + (10x0.5) = \mathbf{35}$$

72) C

All LEED BD+C projects, excluding the residential portion of a building, should provide at least one on-site shower room with a changing facility for the first 100 regular building occupants and one additional shower for every 150 occupants after those first 100. Therefore, one shower room will be needed for projects up to 100 regular building occupants. Two shower rooms will be needed for projects up to 250 regular building occupants. Three shower rooms will be needed for projects up to 400 regular building occupants. And four shower rooms will be needed for projects up to 550 regular building occupants.

73) A

In order to classify building materials according to their solar emissions and reflectance, the **solar reflectance index** will be used for roofing materials, and **solar reflectance** values will be used for nonroof materials (such as hardscape) in this credit's calculations. In addition to the initial SR and SRI values, three-year-aged SR and SRI values will also be needed since the materials' performance will drop as they age.

74) C

Under the Quality Views credit, all LEED BD+C projects—except LEED BD+C: Warehouses and Distribution Centers and LEED BD+C: Healthcare—should achieve a direct line of sight to the outdoors via vision glazing for **75% of all the regularly occupied floor area**.

LEED BD+C: Warehouses and Distribution Centers projects basically have the same view requirements. However, those requirements are only applicable to the office portion of the building. And for the bulk storage, sorting, and distribution areas, projects should meet the view requirements for only 25% of the regularly occupied floor area.

For LEED BD+C: Healthcare projects, the view requirements are applicable to the inpatient units. And those projects can also earn an extra point by satisfying the additional perimeter floor area requirements.

75) A and C

Under the Light Pollution Reduction credit, there are two options for both the "uplight" and "light trespass" requirements.

Projects need to meet uplight and light trespass requirements by either using the **backlight-uplight-glare (BUG) method** in option 1 or the **calculation method** in option 2. Projects may also use different options for uplight and light trespass. For example, a project may choose the BUG method (option1) for meeting the uplight requirements and choose the calculation method (option 2) for meeting the light trespass requirements. In addition to these requirements, projects also need to meet internally illuminated signage requirements if signage exists on-site.

76) D

Under this credit, for <u>all the occupied spaces</u>, projects should meet the requirements for HVAC background noise, sound isolation, reverberation time, and sound reinforcement/masking (if installed in the project). Site exterior noise should be addressed by healthcare projects, not by new construction projects.

77) B
When calculating the walking distance between the building and any destination, the project team should use the shortest path analysis and measure the distance along infrastructure that is safe and comfortable for pedestrians (such as sidewalks and crosswalks).

78) D

79) A
In the Option 2: Envelope Commissioning part of the Enhanced Commissioning credit, project teams should commission the building envelope in accordance with ASHRAE Guideline 0-2005 and the **National Institute of Building Sciences (NIBS) Guideline 3-2012**, Exterior Enclosure Technical Requirements for the Commissioning Process as they relate to energy, water, indoor environmental quality, and durability.

80) C
Under the Quality Views credit, vision glazing should provide a clear image of the exterior and should not be obstructed by <u>frits</u>, <u>fibers</u>, <u>patterned glazing</u>, or <u>added tints that distort color balance</u>.

81) A, C, and E
Under the **Sensitive Land Protection credit**, the development footprint or a portion of it should not be located on prime farmland, unique farmland, or farmland of statewide or local importance, which is defined by the US Department of Agriculture, US Code of Federal Regulations Title 7, Volume 6, Parts 400 to 699, Section 657.5 and identified in a state <u>Natural Resources Conservation Service soil survey</u>.

Under the **Site Assessment credit**, project teams should determine the soil classification with <u>Natural Resources Conservation Service soils delineation</u> (which is a soil survey showing all the different types of soils), determine the US Department of Agriculture prime farmland status, healthy soils, disturbed soils, and previous development on-site.

And remember that under the **Site Development—Protect or Restore Habitat credit**, imported topsoils, or soil blends designed to serve as topsoil, cannot include either of the following:
- Soils defined regionally by the <u>Natural Resources Conservation Service web soil survey</u> (or equivalent for projects outside the United States) as prime farmland, unique farmland, or farmland of statewide or local importance
- Soils from other greenfield sites unless they are a byproduct of a construction process

82) B

83) B and C

One important thing to note is that project teams cannot include the nonpotable water sources (such as harvested rainwater, reclaimed water, or graywater) under the Indoor Water Use Reduction and Outdoor Water Use Reduction prerequisites. However, nonpotable water sources can be included under the Outdoor Water Use Reduction and Indoor Water Use Reduction credits.

And since the Rainwater Management credit is about implementing strategies to manage the on-site rainwater without directing it to the storm sewer system, rainwater harvesting would seriously contribute to this credit.

84) B

85) B

To qualify as a biobased product under the Option 2: Leadership Extraction Practices part of the Building Product Disclosure and Optimization—Sourcing of Raw Materials credit, the product must meet the **Sustainable Agriculture Network's Sustainable Agriculture Standard**. Biobased raw materials must be tested using ASTM Test Method D6866 and be legally harvested. Hide products, such as leather and other animal skin material, are excluded.

Under the Option 2: Leadership Extraction Practices part of the Building Product Disclosure and Optimization—Sourcing of Raw Materials credit, the Forest Stewardship Council (FSC) standard is applicable to wood products, not to biobased products.

On the other hand, GreenScreen is a method used to identify chemicals of high concern and also safer alternatives to those chemicals, and it is referred to under the Building Product Disclosure and Optimization—Chemical Ingredients credit.

Also, LEED requires products that have product-specific declarations with a publicly available, critically reviewed life-cycle assessment conforming to ISO 14044 and having at least a cradle to gate scope assessment under the Building Product Disclosure and Optimization—Environmental Product Declarations credit.

86) A

For the Daylight credit's calculations, under all the options, all LEED BD+C projects except LEED BD+C: Healthcare should consider the **regularly occupied floor area** while the LEED BD+C: Healthcare projects should consider the **perimeter floor area**.

Perimeter floor area is the floor area within 15 feet (4.5 meters) of the perimeter. And it is important to note that for healthcare projects, the perimeter floor area will also be necessary under the Quality Views credit calculations.

To illustrate the "perimeter floor area", let's think about two design alternatives in which the first one is a square floor plan and the second one is a narrow-rectangle floor plan.

The square building will contain a big core area that will not be exposed to any views or daylight, and only the spaces at the perimeter will have access to outside views and daylight.

In the narrow-rectangle building, if the corridor is placed in the middle of the floor plan, all the rooms can have access to quality views or daylight. The following illustrations demonstrate the difference between these design alternatives. The white portions show the spaces with outside views or daylight, while the black areas are the spaces without any views or daylight. Note that the total floor area is the same in both of the design alternatives.

Square building configuration — 64% of the total floor area can have access to outside views or daylight

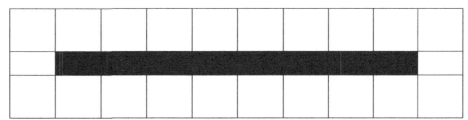

Narrow rectangle building configuration — more than 90% of the total floor area can have access to outside views or daylight

To summarize, the narrow rectangle building will contain more perimeter flor area as compared to the square building, even though they have the same total floor area.

However, it is also important to note that the initial cost of the narrow-rectangle building will be higher than the square building. Since the narrow-rectangle building has more perimeter length, the building will contain more exterior elements.

The same rule will apply to two buildings with the same configuration but with different floor areas. If the total floor area of the narrow-rectangle building in the previous illustration increases (while maintaining the ratio), the total area with access to outdoor views will also decrease.

This is the reason that the floor area and the floor layout are the top priorities to consider when designing for daylight and quality views.

87) C

Under the Sensitive Land Protection credit's option 2, LEED restricts development within **100 feet (30 meters)** of water bodies, with the exception of some minor improvements. And for wetlands, no development can be made within 50 feet (15 meters), with the exception of some minor improvements.

88) B

Under the Sensitive Land Protection credit, trees that meet any of the following ratings can be removed:

- Trees that are under 40% condition rating
- Trees whose diameters are less than 6 inches (150 millimeters) at breast height
- Hazardous trees
- Up to 75% of dead trees
- Up to 20% of the trees whose diameters are more than 6 inches (150 millimeters) at breast height, with a condition rating of 40% or higher

The tree conditions mentioned above must be assessed by an arborist certified by the International Society of Arboriculture (ISA), and ISA measures should be used (or a local equivalent for projects outside the United States).

89) C

Retail projects should provide at least two (not one) short-term bicycle storage spaces for every 5,000 square feet (465 square meters). There cannot be fewer than two storage spaces per building.

Minimum number of short-term bicycle storage spaces = 2 x (50,000 / 5,000) = **20**

For this questions, the number of peak visitors is not needed to determine the short-term bicycle storage spaces for LEED BD+C: Retail projects.

90) B

One point will be awarded for each Regional Priority credit achieved, up to a maximum of four.

91) C

The Optimize Energy Performance <u>credit</u> has two options: the first option is the Whole-Building Energy Simulation, and the second option is Prescriptive Compliance with the ASHRAE Advanced Energy Design Guide. Project teams pursuing option 1 of the credit should pursue option 1 of this prerequisite and create an energy model to be used for both the Minimum Energy Performance prerequisite and the Optimize Energy Performance credit. Project teams pursuing option 2 of the credit should also pursue option 2 of the prerequisite.

Projects pursuing option 3 of the prerequisite will not be eligible to pursue the Optimize Energy Performance credit because that credit is basically a continuation of the Minimum Energy Performance prerequisite and it does not contain an option 3.

92) C

93) A

Under the Light Pollution Reduction credit, the following types of lighting are exempt from the credit requirements if they are controlled separately from the nonexempt lighting:

- Specialized signal, directional, and marker lighting for transportation
- Lighting solely used for facade and landscape lighting in MLO lighting zones 3 and 4 and that is automatically turned off from midnight to six in the morning
- Government-mandated roadway lighting
- Lighting for theatrical purposes, stages, and video performances
- Hospital emergency department and helipad lighting
- **National flag lighting in MLO lighting zones 2, 3, or 4**

94) B

Note that under the Construction Indoor Air Quality Management Plan credit, **healthcare** projects are subject to different requirements compared with other rating systems.

95) C

Low-impact development (LID) is an approach to mimic natural systems and to manage the storm water closest to its source. LID strategies include decreasing impervious surfaces and increasing vegetation on-site. In addition, LID works on slowing down the flow of rainwater out of site and makes sure the rainwater does not get contaminated.

Using materials with higher SR and SRI values contributes to reducing the heat island effect rather than rainwater management.

96) B

To qualify as a bicycle network, a network should be continuous and consist of any combination of the following:

- Off-street bicycle paths or trails at least 8 feet (2.5 meters) wide for a two-way path and at least 5 feet (1.5 meters) wide for a one-way path
- Physically designated on-street bicycle lanes that are at least 5 feet (1.5 meters) wide
- Streets that are designed for a target speed of 25 mph (40 kmh)

97) D

LEED directly addresses VOC levels of the materials used inside the building under the Low-Emitting Materials credit.

98) A

The Site Master Plan credit is only applicable to school projects, not to healthcare projects.

99) C

In the Optimize Energy Performance credit's option 1, new construction projects can use their whole building energy simulations (if they choose to create them by pursuing option 1 of the prerequisite) and make further reductions from their baseline energy use from **6%** to **50%**.

Since in the Minimum Energy Performance prerequisite, new construction projects are required to establish a 5% energy use reduction, in the credit they need to establish a minimum of 6% energy use reduction, up to 50%. The greater the percentage of energy use reduction, the higher the points awarded.

100) C

The Innovation credit can be a straightforward credit, but it is strongly recommended to know it thoroughly. Below is the number of points awarded under the Option 3: Additional Strategies part of the Innovation credit:

Innovation—1–3 Points
Pilot—1–3 points
Exemplary performance—1–2 points

However, if the question asked how many points could be earned by the pursuit of pilot credits under the Innovation credit, then the answer would be 4 points. That's because option 2 of the Innovation credit additionally provides 1 point for pursuing a pilot credit.

APPENDIX A – SUMMARY OF ASHRAE STANDARDS

Name of the Standard / Program	Keywords	Related Prerequisites / Credits
ASHRAE Guideline 0-2005	Commissioning essentials	Prerequisite — Fundamental Comm. and Ver., Credit — Enhanced Commissioning
ASHRAE Guideline 1.1-2007	HVAC & R technical requirements for commissioning	Prerequisite — Fundamental Comm. and Ver., Credit — Enhanced Commissioning
ANSI/ASHRAE/IESNA Standard 90.1.-2010, Appendix G with Errata	Used for the whole building energy simulation under option 1	Prerequisite — Minimum Energy Perf., Credit — Optimize Energy Perf.
ANSI/ASHRAE/IESNA Standard 90.1-2010, with errata	Used for all options	Prerequisite — Minimum Energy Perf., Credit — Optimize Energy Perf.
ASHRAE Advanced Energy Design Guide	Used under option 2	Prerequisite — Minimum Energy Perf., Credit — Optimize Energy Perf.
ASHRAE 90.1-2010, Appendix B	Energy standard for buildings, also used to identify project's climate zone	Prerequisite — Minimum Energy Performance
ANSI/ASHRAE/IESNA Standard 90.1–2010, Appendixes B and D	Energy standard for buildings, also used to identify international project's climate zone	Prerequisite — Minimum Energy Performance
ANSI/ASHRAE/IESNA Standard 90.1-2010, G2.5	Used for the exceptional calculation method	Prerequisite — Minimum Energy Performance

Name of the Standard / Program	Keywords	Related Prerequisites / Credits
ASHRAE 62.1-2010	Ventilation for acceptable indoor air quality	Prerequisite — Minimum Air Quality Perf., Credit — Enhanced IAQ Strategies
ASHRAE Standard 170–2008	Used to address the mechanical ventilation requirements of the healthcare projects	Prerequisite — Minimum Air Quality Performance
ASHRAE 52.2-2007	Air filter standards	Credit — Enhanced Indoor Air Quality Strategies, Credit — Construction Indoor Air Quality Management Plan
ASHRAE Standard 55–2010	Thermal comfort conditions for human occupancy	Credit — Thermal Comfort
2011 ASHRAE Handbook	Handbook about the HVAC applications, in the credit it relates to the HVAC background noise	Credit — Acoustic Performance

APPENDIX B — IMPORTANT STANDARDS AND PROGRAMS

Name of the Standard / Program	Keywords	Related Prerequisites / Credits
ANSI Consensus National Standard Guide 2.0	Useful for implementing a successful integrative process	Prerequisite—Integrative Project Planning and Design, Credit—Integrative Process
US Department of Agriculture, US Code of Federal Regulations Title 7, Volume 6	Defines prime farmlands	Credit—Sensitive Land Protection
Natural Resources Conservation Service (NRCS)	Soil survey	Credit—Sensitive Land Protection, Credit—Site Assessment
Federal Emergency Management Agency (FEMA)	Defines flood hazard areas	Credit—Sensitive Land Protection
US Endangered Species Act	Defines threatened and endangered species	Credit—Sensitive Land Protection
NatureServe	Classifies species and ecological communities	Credit—Sensitive Land Protection
International Union of Conservation of Nature Red List	Alternative to NatureServe	Credit—Sensitive Land Protection
US EPA National Priority List	Defines National Priority sites	Credit—High Priority Site
US Housing and Urban Development	Defines Federal Empowerment Zone, Federal Enterprise Community, and Federal Renewal Community	Credit—High Priority Site

Name of the Standard / Program	Keywords	Related Prerequisites / Credits
US Department of Treasury, Community Development Financial Institutions Fund	Provides funds for low-income communities	Credit—High Priority Site
Parking Consultants Council, Transportation Planning Handbook, 3rd edition	Provides base parking capacity ratios for buildings	Credit—Reduced Parking Footprint
American Council for an Energy-Efficient Economy (ACEEE)	Defines green vehicles (should score a minimum of 45 on ACEEE to qualify)	Credit—Green Vehicles
Illuminating Engineering Society of North America (IESNA)	Develops lighting specifications	Credit—Light Pollution Reduction
2012 US EPA, Construction General Permit (CGP)	Sets requirements for the erosion and sedimentation control (ESC) plan	Prerequisite—Construction Activity Pollution Prevention
TR-55 initial water storage capacity	Projects can model the watersheds to calculate the storm water runoff volume, peak rate of discharge and storage volumes	Site Assessment—Credit
Land Trust Alliance	Provides accreditation to land trust organizations	Credit—Site Development - Protect or Restore Habitat
US Environmental Protection Agency Technical Guidance on Implementing the Stormwater Runoff Requirements for Federal Projects under Section 438 of the Energy Independence and Security Act	Methodology used for the rainwater management calculations	Credit—Rainwater Management
National Climatic Data Center	Provides historical rainfall data	Credit—Rainwater Management

Name of the Standard / Program	Keywords	Related Prerequisites / Credits
Illuminating Engineering Society and International Dark Sky Association (IES/IDA) Model Lighting Ordinance (MLO) User Guide	Used to determine the lighting zone of the project	Credit—Light Pollution Reduction
US Environmental Protection Agency WaterSense Water Budget Tool	Calculates landscape water requirements (LWR)	Prerequisite, Credit—Outdoor Water Use Reduction
Energy Policy Act of 1992 (EPAct 1992)	Specifies baseline flow and flush rates	Prerequisite, Credit—Indoor Water Use Reduction
WaterSense	A program developed by EPA to identify high-performance, water-efficient fixtures and fittings	Prerequisite, Credit—Indoor Water Use Reduction
ENERGY STAR Portfolio Manager™	Interactive, online management tool that enables projects to track and assess energy and water consumption	
ENERGY STAR TargetFinder™	Allows projects to set target goals for building design's energy demands	
Home Energy Saver™	A do-it-yourself energy audit, which is developed by the US Department of Energy for existing buildings to analyze, reduce, and manage their energy use	
Montreal Protocol	Banned the production of chlorofluorocarbon (CFC) refrigerants and also phasing out hydrochlorofluorocarbon (HCFC) refrigerants	
Advanced Buildings™ Core Performance Guide™	Energy design guide	Prerequisite—Minimum Energy Performance
National Institute of Building Sciences (NIBS) Guideline 3-2012, Exterior Enclosure Technical Requirements for the Cx Process	Used for the envelope Commissioning	Credit—Enhanced Commissioning

Name of the Standard / Program	Keywords	Related Prerequisites / Credits
US Department of Energy's Commercial Buildings Energy Consumption Survey (CBECS)	Database used to estimate a building's total energy cost	Credit—Advanced Energy Metering, Credit—Renewable Energy Production, Credit—Green Power and Carbon Offsets
US EPA GreenChill	Provides best practices guideline for leak tightness at installation. Provides store certification.	Credit—Enhanced Refrigerant Management
Green-e	The leading certification program for the green power generation in the United States	Credit—Green Power and Carbon Offsets
Green-e Energy	Green power certification Program	Credit—Green Power and Carbon Offsets
Green-e Climate	Carbon offset certification program	Credit—Green Power and Carbon Offsets
US National Register of Historic Places	Identifies the "historic" designation criteria	Credit—Building Life-Cycle Impact Reduction
Secretary of Interior's Standards for the Treatment of Historic Properties	Sets standards for the treatment of historic properties	Credit—Building Life-Cycle Impact Reduction
Forest Stewardship Council (FSC)	A voluntary program which sets standards to wood product manufacturers to ensure responsible forest management in order to prevent deforestation and loss of habitat	Credit—BPDO Sourcing of Raw Materials
Extended Producer Responsibility (EPR)	Is a product stewardship policy approach that holds consumer goods companies responsible for managing their own products and packaging when consumers are finished with them	Credit—BPDO Sourcing of Raw Materials

Name of the Standard / Program	Keywords	Related Prerequisites / Credits
Sustainable Agriculture Network's Sustainable Agriculture Standard	Standard for bio-based Materials	Credit—BPDO: Sourcing of Raw Materials, Credit—Furniture and Medical Furnishings
Cradle to Cradle Certification (C2C)	Assesses the ingredients of a product according to environmental and human health hazards	Credit—BPDO Material Ingredients
GreenScreen	A method used to identify chemicals of high concern and safer alternatives	Credit—BPDO Material Ingredients
REACH Optimization	European Union's legislation that requires all chemicals sold to be evaluated based on their hazard profiles	Credit—BPDO Material Ingredients
Chartered Institution of Building Services Engineers (CIBSE) Applications Manual	About ventilation strategies	Prerequisite—Minimum Indoor Air Quality Performance, Credit—Enhanced Indoor Air Quality Strategies
National Ambient Air Quality Standards	Standards for exterior contamination prevention	Credit—Enhanced Indoor Air Quality Strategies
California Department of Public Health (CDPH) Standard Method v1.1	General emissions evaluation and VOC testing procedures	Credit—Low Emitting Materials, Credit—Indoor Air Quality Assessment
California Air Resources Board (CARB) 2007, Suggested Control Measure for Architectural Coatings	VOC content requirements for wet-applied products	Credit—Low Emitting Materials
South Coast Air Quality Management District (SCAQMD) Rule 1113	VOC content requirements for wet-applied products	Credit—Low Emitting Materials

Name of the Standard / Program	Keywords	Related Prerequisites / Credits
ANSI/BIFMA Standard Method M7.1-2011	Furniture evaluation	Credit—Low Emitting Materials
Sheet Metal and Air Conditioning National Contractors Association (SMACNA) guidelines	Describes the necessary control measures to be taken during construction to protect indoor air quality	Credit—Construction Indoor Air Quality Management Plan
Windows and Offices; A Study of Office Worker Performance and the Indoor Environment	Defines view factors	Credit—Quality Views

APPENDIX C – PREREQUISITES/CREDITS AND THEIR APPLICABLE RATING SYSTEMS

P/C	Name of the Prerequisite/Credit	Applicable to:
Prerequisite	Integrative Project Planning and Design	Healthcare
Credit	Integrative Process	All LEED BD+C Rating Systems
Credit	LEED for Neighborhood Development Location	All LEED BD+C Rating Systems
Credit	Sensitive Land Protection	All LEED BD+C Rating Systems
Credit	High Priority Site	All LEED BD+C Rating Systems
Credit	Surrounding Density and Diverse Uses	All LEED BD+C Rating Systems
Credit	Access to Quality Transit	All LEED BD+C Rating Systems
Credit	Bicycle Facilities	All LEED BD+C Rating Systems
Credit	Reduced Parking Footprint	All LEED BD+C Rating Systems
Credit	Green Vehicles	All LEED BD+C Rating Systems
Prerequisite	Construction Activity Pollution Prevention	All LEED BD+C Rating Systems
Prerequisite	Environmental Site Assessment	Schools and Healthcare
Credit	Site Assessment	All LEED BD+C Rating Systems
Credit	Site Development–Protect or Restore Habitat	All LEED BD+C Rating Systems
Credit	Open Space	All LEED BD+C Rating Systems
Credit	Rainwater Management	All LEED BD+C Rating Systems
Credit	Heat Island Reduction	All LEED BD+C Rating Systems

P/C	Name of the Prerequisite/Credit	Applicable to:
Credit	Light Pollution Reduction	All LEED BD+C Rating Systems
Credit	Site Master Plan	Schools
Credit	Tenant Design and Construction Guidelines	Core and Shell
Credit	Places of Respite	Healthcare
Credit	Direct Exterior Access	Healthcare
Credit	Joint Use of Facilities	Schools
Prerequisite	Outdoor Water Use Reduction	All LEED BD+C Rating Systems
Prerequisite	Indoor Water Use Reduction	All LEED BD+C Rating Systems
Prerequisite	Building-Level Water Metering	All LEED BD+C Rating Systems
Credit	Outdoor Water Use Reduction	All LEED BD+C Rating Systems
Credit	Indoor Water Use Reduction	All LEED BD+C Rating Systems
Credit	Cooling Tower Water Use	All LEED BD+C Rating Systems
Credit	Water Metering	All LEED BD+C Rating Systems
Prerequisite	Fundamental Commissioning and Verification	All LEED BD+C Rating Systems
Prerequisite	Minimum Energy Performance	All LEED BD+C Rating Systems
Prerequisite	Building Level Energy Metering	All LEED BD+C Rating Systems
Prerequisite	Fundamental Refrigerant Management	All LEED BD+C Rating Systems
Credit	Enhanced Commissioning	All LEED BD+C Rating Systems
Credit	Optimize Energy Performance	All LEED BD+C Rating Systems
Credit	Advanced Energy Metering	All LEED BD+C Rating Systems
Credit	Demand Response	All LEED BD+C Rating Systems
Credit	Renewable Energy Production	All LEED BD+C Rating Systems
Credit	Enhanced Refrigerant Management	All LEED BD+C Rating Systems
Credit	Green Power and Carbon Offsets	All LEED BD+C Rating Systems
Prerequisite	Storage and Collection of Recyclables	All LEED BD+C Rating Systems
Prerequisite	Construction and Demolition Waste Management Planning	All LEED BD+C Rating Systems
Prerequisite	PBT Source Reduction–Mercury	Healthcare
Credit	Building Life-Cycle Impact Reduction	All LEED BD+C Rating Systems
Credit	BPDO–Environmental Product Declarations	All LEED BD+C Rating Systems

P/C	Name of the Prerequisite/Credit	Applicable to:
Credit	BPDO–Sourcing of Raw Materials	All LEED BD+C Rating Systems
Credit	BPDO–Material Ingredients	All LEED BD+C Rating Systems
Credit	PBT Source Reduction–Mercury	Healthcare
Credit	PBT Source Reduction–Lead, Cadmium, and Copper	Healthcare
Credit	Furniture and Medical Furnishings	Healthcare
Credit	Design for Flexibility	Healthcare
Credit	Construction and Demolition Waste Management	All LEED BD+C Rating Systems
Prerequisite	Minimum Indoor Air Quality Performance	All LEED BD+C Rating Systems
Prerequisite	Environmental Tobacco Smoke Control	All LEED BD+C Rating Systems
Prerequisite	Minimum Acoustic Performance	Schools
Credit	Enhanced Indoor Air Quality Strategies	All LEED BD+C Rating Systems
Credit	Low–Emitting Materials	All LEED BD+C Rating Systems
Credit	Construction Indoor Air Quality Management Plan	All LEED BD+C Rating Systems
Credit	Indoor Air Quality Assessment	All LEED BD+C Rating Systems, except Core and Shell
Credit	Thermal Comfort	All LEED BD+C Rating Systems, except Core and Shell
Credit	Interior Lighting	All LEED BD+C Rating Systems, except Core and Shell
Credit	Daylight	All LEED BD+C Rating Systems
Credit	Quality Views	All LEED BD+C Rating Systems
Credit	Acoustic Performance	All LEED BD+C Rating Systems, except Core and Shell and Retail
Credit	Innovation	All LEED BD+C Rating Systems
Credit	LEED Accredited Professional	All LEED BD+C Rating Systems
Credit	Regional Priority	All LEED BD+C Rating Systems

40/60 rule: A method used to choose the appropriate rating system for the project if the project seems to fit under multiple rating systems.

Active daylighting: Is a system that tracks and collects the sunlight using mechanical devices, but they may not function well on cloudy days.

Adapted plants: Types of plants that do not occur naturally in a specific location; however, they can nonetheless adapt easily to the climate of the region.

Adjacent site: A site containing a previously developed site at its minimum 25% of the boundary bordering parcels.

Albedo: A type of reflectivity measurement from "0" to "1," which "0" represents black surfaces that absorb all the solar radiation, while "1" represents white surfaces that reflects all the solar radiation.

Alternative compliance paths (ACPs): Enable international projects to earn the appropriate prerequisites/credits by allowing them to meet international standards or their local standards instead of United States based standards.

Alternative fuel vehicles: Vehicles that consume nongasoline, low-polluting fuels like hydrogen, electricity, propane, compressed natural gas, liquid natural gas, methanol, or ethanol.

Alternative fuel: Low-polluting fuels like hydrogen, electricity, propane, compressed natural gas, liquid natural gas, methanol, or ethanol.

Alternative water source: Nonpotable water from on-site surfaces, or freshwater sources, such as graywater, on-site reclaimed water, collected rainwater, captured condensate, and rejected water from reverse osmosis systems. Water from public utilities is excluded.

Basis of design (BOD): Describes the information necessary to accomplish the owner's project requirements, which includes system requirements, design criteria, standards, and guidelines, developed by the architect/engineer.

Bio-based materials: Are products other than food that are biological products, renewable agricultural materials or forestry materials. Biobased materials are derived from biomass. Plants and animals can be an example of biobased materials, however, hide products, such as leather and other animal skin material are excluded in LEED calculations.

Biofuel: Fuels produced from organic material. Biofuel includes untreated wood waste, landfill gas, agricultural crops or waste, animal waste, and other types of organic waste.

Bioswale: A stormwater control feature which uses a combination of engineered basin, soils and vegetation.

Blackwater: Is the term to describe the used water that has come into contact with waste. Thus, the water collected from the urinals and toilets can be classified as blackwater.

Blowdown: Removal of the cooling tower's water in order to minimize deposit of scales.

Brownfield site: A previously developed site that was contaminated with waste or pollution. A site that is left from an abandoned building in which the contamination is not yet known can also be classified as a brownfield site.

BUG rating method: A luminaire classification system that classifies a luminaire according to backlight, uplight, and glare.

Building automation system (BAS): A computer-based monitoring system which can monitor, coordinate and control every individual building system.

Building exterior: Defined as everything from the waterproofing membrane, inclusive of the waterproofing membrane.

Building footprint: Describes the area that the building sits on.

Building interior: Defined as everything inside the waterproofing membrane.

Built environment: Refers to all the man-made surroundings that are needed for human activity, from roads, to buildings, to neighborhoods.

Carbon neutrality: To emit no more carbon emissions than can realistically be offset.

Carbon offset: Is a reduction of carbon dioxide (CO_2) made in order to compensate, or offset an equivalent carbon dioxide (CO_2) emission made elsewhere.

Chain of custody (CoC): Procedure of tracking a product from extraction/harvesting to its distribution. An example may be the FSC certification, which provides chain-of-custody certification for wood-based products.

Charrettes: Are intense workshops that are generally held at the beginning of the project and during the project milestones.

Chlorofluorocarbon (CFC)-based refrigerant: A refrigerant in fluid state containing hydrocarbons, which absorb heat at low temperatures and reject heat at higher temperatures.

Clean waste: Materials that are left over from construction and demolition that are nonhazardous.

Closed system: System that does not produce any waste product at the end by circulating the same median.

Commingled waste: Single-streamed waste for recycling.

Commissioning (Cx): Is a systematic investigation by skilled personnel that compares building performance with the project goals, design specifications, and, most importantly, the owner's project requirements (OPR).

Conventional irrigation: Common system used for irrigation, such as irrigation through sprinkler heads above the ground.

Corporate Sustainability Reports (CSR): Provides information about the manufacturer or raw-material supplier of a product that has been verified to employ sustainable principles during the creation of their products.

Cradle-to-cradle: Evaluates materials to have infinite life cycles through recycling to form a closed system.

Cradle-to-grave: Investigates materials from their extraction to their disposal.

Cradle-to-gate assessment: Evaluates a product's partial life cycle from its resource extraction/harvesting to becoming a manufactured product ready for sale at the factory gate.

Current facility requirements (CFR): Requirements to fulfill the owner's operational needs.

Demand response (DR): An intentional reduction in the electricity usage in response to a demand response (DR) event, or changes in the price of electricity.

Demand response event (curtailment event): The period that the utility company asks for a reduction in electricity usage from its program participants.

Development footprint: Named for the sum of all the areas that are affected by the project's activity in the project site. Permeable pavements, at least 50% permeable, are exempt.

District energy system (DES): A central energy conversion plant that provides thermal energy, shared by a group of buildings.

Diverse use: Publicly available businesses that provide daily need goods or services. According to USGBC, diverse uses do not include ATMs, vending machines and touch screens.

Diversion rate: Percentage of waste materials diverted from landfill.

Drip irrigation systems: Are the types of microirrigation systems that drip water to the roots of plants to minimize the use of irrigation water and fertilizers. They are the most water-efficient systems and have very short payback periods.

Dry ponds (detention ponds): Hold the excess rainwater for some time, thereby allowing the rainwater to slowly seep into the ground without contamination. Dry ponds are excavated areas that detain and slow down stormwater but are dry at other times.

EDUCATION @USGBC: Education portal of USGBC.

Embodied energy: The total energy consumed resulting from a product's manufacturing, transportation, installation, and use.

Emergent properties: Emergence of certain properties in the systems as a result of interaction of individual elements.

Emissivity (infrared or thermal emittance): Is a measure that shows how much heat or infrared radiation a material can shed back into the atmosphere.

Energy rater: Professionals with a HERS rater credential that conducts the performance testing in LEED for Homes projects.

Energy use intensity (EUI): A measurement unit that describes the building's energy usage relative to its size.

Environmental Product Declaration (EPD): Disclosure that looks at the entire life cycle of a product and assesses the cost of the product on the environment. Products that contain an EPD will give information about a product's impact on global warming, ozone depletion, water pollution, greenhouse gas emission, human toxicity, and more.

Erosion and sedimentation control (ESC) plan: A plan developed to prevent erosion, sedimentation, and stormwater pollution to the water bodies, wetlands, and the whole neighborhood.

Evapotranspiration: Is the term used for the return of water to the atmosphere through evaporation from plants.

Extended Producer Responsibility (EPR): Is a product stewardship policy approach that holds companies producing consumer goods responsible for managing their own products and packaging when consumers are finished with them.

Extensive vegetated roofs: Are the types of roofs that do not include a variety of plants and require little maintenance. Their soil layer is thinner compared with the intensive roofs since they are more designed for the smaller-sized vegetation.

Floor-to-area ratio (FAR): Is calculated by dividing the total square feet of a building by the total square feet of the lot of the building.

Flush-out: Is the process of supplying good amounts of fresh air to the building before or during occupancy to take away the contaminated air and establish the desired level of indoor air quality.

Foot-candle: A measure of the amount of illumination that falls on a surface, equal to one lumen per square foot.

Functional entry: Any building opening that is open and used by pedestrians during business hours.

Gallons per flush (gpf): A unit of measurement used to calculate the water usage of flush fixtures such as toilets and urinals.

Gallons per minute (gpm): A unit of measurement used to calculate the water usage of flow fixtures such as sink faucets, shower heads, and aerators.

Geothermal heat pumps: Also known as "geoexchange", or "ground source heat pumps," geothermal heat pumps are central heating and/or cooling systems that transfer heat to or from the ground. In winter, this system uses the earth as a heat source while in summer, the earth is used as a heat sink.

Graywater: Is the untreated household water that did not come into contact with toilet waste. Used water from bathtubs, showers, bathroom washbasins, and water from clothes washers and laundry tubs can be examples of graywater and may be used as a flush water in toilets or urinals. This definition can change depending on the local codes.

Green building: According to the US Environmental Protection Agency, green building is the practice of creating structures and using processes that are environmentally responsible and resource-efficient throughout a building's life cycle, from siting to design, construction, operation, maintenance, renovation, and deconstruction. This practice expands and complements the classical building design concerns of economy, utility, durability, and comfort.

Green cleaning program : Specifies the green building products to be used (such as products that meet Green Seal, Environmental Choice, or EPA standards), chemicals allowed to be used inside the building, training of the cleaning personnel for the use of chemicals and green cleaning practices, indoor pest control plans, and energy-efficient cleaning equipment.

Green cleaning: The use of environmentally friendly products by also employing environmentally friendly cleaning principles in cleaning.

Green infrastructure: Infrastructure to direct the rainwater collected from the impervious surfaces to the vegetation and soil surfaces without routing them to the storm sewer system.

Green power: Off-site renewable energy.

Green vehicles: Vehicles that achieve a minimum green score of 45 on the American Council for an Energy Efficient Economy (ACEEE) annual vehicle rating guide (or a local equivalent for projects outside the United States.)

Greenfield: The term used to define undeveloped land.

Greenwashing: Refers to the presentation of a product or a material as being more environmentally friendly than it actually is.

Halons: Chemicals used in fire suppression systems.

Hard cost: Costs that physically contribute to the construction, such as labor costs, the cost of construction materials, and equipment.

Health Product Declaration (HPD): Disclosure that provides a product's material ingredients, list of potential chemicals, related concerns, and additional health information.

Heat island effect: Dark colored, nonreflective surfaces absorb heat during hot weather and release it into the atmosphere, and this releasing of heat is called the heat island effect.

Home Energy Rater (HERS Rater): Energy rater credential administered by the Residential Energy Services Network (RESNET).

Home size adjustment (HSA): In the LEED for Homes rating system, points are adjusted in all the categories according to the square footage of the home. Thus, homes that are bigger need to earn more points to achieve a LEED certification while smaller-sized homes can become LEED-certified by earning fewer points. Other LEED rating systems do not have size adjustments.

Impervious surface: A surface that contains less than 50% perviousness.

Indoor air quality management plan: A plan developed to protect the indoor air quality for construction workers and building occupants.

Infill sites: Or infill developments, are sites that at least 75% of their site area were either previously developed or were already being used for other purposes in the urban areas.

Inherently nonemitting materials: Materials with very low or no VOC content.

Integrated pest management (IPM): A sustainable approach that combines knowledge about pests, nature, pest prevention, and control methods that minimize pest infestation and damage while minimizing hazards to the building occupants, the property itself, and the environment.

Integrated process: Emphasizes the importance of connection and communication among all the professionals and stakeholders in the project.

Intensive vegetated roofs: Contain wider variety of plants and which contain more soil depth to support those plants.

Invasive plants: The types of plants that spread and damage the environment by taking over the adjacent existing native and adapted plants.

Land trust: A nonprofit organization that works on conserving lands.

Landscape water requirement (LWR): Is the amount of water that the landscape of the site will require during the site's peak watering month.

LEED AP with specialty: LEED credential, created for professionals with advanced knowledge in green building practices and specialized in a particular LEED rating system.

LEED Campus Program: Used to certify multiple projects that are located on a single campus and which are owned by the same entity.

LEED combined review: A type of LEED certification review in which the documentation for all the design and construction prerequisites/credits are submitted for review at the end of the construction phase (for LEED BD+C and LEED ID+C rating systems).

LEED Fellow: LEED credential created to designate the most exceptional professionals in the green building industry, it is the most prestigious designation awarded.

LEED for Homes Green Rater: Professional who provides in-field verification to LEED for Homes projects. (The other rating systems do not require any in-field verification.)

LEED for Homes Provider Organization: Responsible to oversee all the certification process and incorporate the LEED for Homes rating system requirements into the project's design and construction.

LEED Green Associate: LEED credential created for professionals with a proven, up-to-date understanding of green building principles and practices.

LEED impact categories: Also called system goals, are the key elements that every LEED project aims to accomplish, and it consists of 7 items.

LEED project boundary: Portion of the site submitted for LEED certification. Defined by the platted property line of the project, including all land and water within it.

LEED recertification: Necessary for LEED O+M projects to continue their certification every 5 years. LEED certification granted to projects under the other LEED rating systems do not need a recertification.

LEED split review: A type of LEED certification review in which the design prerequisites/credits are submitted for review during the design phase, and both the additional design prerequisites/credits and all the construction prerequisites/credits are submitted at the end of the construction phase (for LEED BD+C and LEED ID+C rating systems).

LEED Pro Reviewer: Professionals that evaluate the educational LEED courses on EDUCATION @USGBC.

LEED Volume Program: A streamlined certification process for organizations that plan to certify more than 25 prototype-based construction projects within 3 years.

Leverage point: The point where any action taken in the system can bring about significant results.

Life-cycle approach: Evaluates the entire life of a project, product, or service.

Life-cycle assessment (LCA): Evaluates all the environmental effects of a product quantitatively for the whole lifetime of that material.

Life-cycle costing (LCC): Assesses a product's total cost for the whole lifetime of the product by evaluating both the initial price and the operating costs.

Light shelves: Are horizontal, light-reflecting overhangs that are positioned to reflect the daylight into the desired area of the building.

Light tubes: Also called sun tubes or sun pipes, are structures that are used to transport sunlight inside a building.

Linear approach: An approach of the conventional building process, in which a project team member completes a work individually and then passes it to the next person.

Load shedding: Is the intentional action by the power utility to reduce the load in the power system in order prevent a total failure of the system.

Load shifting: Is storing the energy generated during off-peak hours, in order to use it during the peak-demand hours.

Long-term bicycle storage: Protected storage from rain and snow for the use of residents and employees.

Low-impact development (LID): An approach to mimic natural systems and to manage the stormwater closest to its source.

Makeup water: Water used to replace the lost water in open systems.

Masking systems: Or sound masking systems, are equipments used to reduce the background noise in spaces.

Minimum efficiency reporting value (MERV): Rates the air filters according to their performance on removing particles from air.

Minimum program requirements (MPRs): Provide guidance on the types of projects that are eligible for LEED certification, protect the integrity of the LEED program, and reduce the number of issues that arise during the certification process.

Monitor based commissioning (MBCx): Is the process of utilizing a software that will monitor real-time data from the building automation system and building meters.

Mulching: A protective layer applied to the surface of soil that will help to keep the roots of the plants cool and therefore prevent evaporation.

Native plants (indigenous plants): Are the type of plants that occur and develop naturally in a specific location.

Natural refrigerants: Refrigerants that occur in nature's biological and chemical cycles without human involvement, such as carbon dioxide (CO_2), water (H_2O), ammonia (NH_3), air, and hydrocarbons such as propane, ethane, and butane.

Negative feedback loops: A change brings an additional change in the opposite direction. If a room gets warmer than the set temperature, the thermostat will send a signal to the air conditioning, and the air conditioning will stop blowing warm air.

Net-zero energy project: A project that only use its own generated renewable energy.

Nonpoint source pollution: Type of pollution in which its source cannot be identified and which generally results from multiple sources.

Nonpotable water: Water that does not meet the human consumption standards.

Nonprocess energy (regulated energy): The energy consumed by the items that are used to condition spaces and maintain comfort and amenities for building occupants.

Open systems: Systems that constantly consume other items, use them, and produce waste at the end.

Open-grid pavement: A pavement system with at least 50% unbound.

Passive daylighting: Is a system that both collects the sunlight using static and nonmoving items such as windows, glass doors, some skylights, light tubes, and light shelves.

Pilot Credits: Credits being tested for the updated version of LEED.

Places of respite: An area in a natural environment, dedicated to connecting patients and visitors, in the hospitals.

Plug loads (receptacle load): Represents the electrical use by all the equipment that is connected to the electrical system via electrical receptacles.

Positive feedback loop: A producing B, which in turn produces more of A. An example of this would be an interest-earning savings account. As the account grows, more interest is earned which in turn brings further account growth.

Postconsumer recycled content: Is the recycled content of a used material. For example, recyclable printer paper can be sent to recycling after being used and can become a part of new printer paper. Other types of materials with postconsumer recycled content can be aluminum cans, water bottles, most glass, wood and steel products, newspapers, and more.

Potable water: Water that is approved for human use that meets or exceeds US Environmental Protection Agency drinking water quality standards (or a local equivalent outside the United States.)

Preconsumer recycled content: Is the content of a material that is recycled before getting used by any consumer. An example may be a sawdust generated during the manufacturing of a wood product that is recycled to be used inside an MDF board (medium density fiberboard).

Preferred parking: Parking spaces that are closest to the main entrance of a building.

Prerequisites: The minimum requirements that all buildings under a certain rating system must meet in order to achieve LEED certification.

Previously developed site: A site that contains at least 75% previously developed land.

Prime farmland: Land that is used for producing food, feed, forage, fiber, and oilseed crops or is available for these uses, as determined by the US Department of Agriculture's Natural Resources Conservation Service.

Prius effect: People can respond to something only if they have real-time information about it.

Process water: Is the type of water used by mechanical or other types of systems in buildings such as cooling towers or medical equipment in hospitals.

Radon: Is a radioactive gas that is naturally found in the soils, rocks, and water bodies that is harmful to human health.

Rainwater harvesting: An aspect of rainwater management that collects and filters the rainwater to be reused as an alternative to potable water.

Rapidly renewable materials: Natural materials that can replenish within 10 years.

Reclaimed water: Is the former blackwater that has been treated and purified for reuse.

Reference soils: Are the native soils of a site.

Refrigerant: Substances used to transfer heat.

Regenerative design: Is a type of building design that creates no waste and also provides more output than consumed input.

Renewable energy certificates (RECs): Or green tags, represent a tradable, nontangible commodity associated with the qualities of renewable energy generation. REC is a proof that, when purchased, an amount of energy was created using renewable energy sources.

Renewable energy: A type of energy that is derived from renewable sources. Renewable energy includes solar, wind, wave, biomass, and geothermal power, plus certain forms of hydropower.

Reverberation time: Is the time span between when a sound is produced and when it dies away.

Scope 1 energy: Relates to the direct energy from the owned or controlled sources.

Scope 2 energy: Energy that relates to the purchased energy.

Scope 3 energy: Relates to the energies that are not owned or directly controlled.

Sensitive lands: Ecologically sensitive areas such as prime farmland, floodplain, habitat, water bodies, or wetland.

Short-term bicycle storage: Typically used by visitors for less than two hours that typically does not provide enclosed parking.

Simple box energy modeling: A preliminary building model used to assess the building's energy loads.

Site assessment: Is a part of the integrative process, which clearly shows the project teams the properties of the site, including its topography, hydrology, climate, soil types, water availability, and human health effects.

Skylights: Are horizontal elements in the roof of the buildings that are made of opaque materials (mostly glass) to allow sunlight into the building.

Smart growth: A neighborhood development approach that protects undeveloped lands and contributes to project development in locations near jobs, schools, shops, and other diverse uses.

Soft cost: Covers everything needed for developing a project that does not physically contribute to the building. All the management and supervision costs, design costs, permits, and taxes can be seen as the soft costs.

Softscape: Part of a landscape that consists of live horticultural elements.

Solar reflectance (SR) value: Shows the solar energy that is reflected by a surface on a scale of 0 to 1. A black surface will have a SR of 0while a white surface will have a SR of 1.

Solar reflectance index (SRI) value: Indicates a material's ability to stay cool by reflecting solar radiation and emitting thermal radiation. Thus, both the solar reflectance and emissivity of a material will be combined to rank the material.

Source reduction: Refers to the exact sizing of the materials to be produced through prefabrication, modular construction, or similar methods, in order to prevent waste.

Spatial daylight autonomy (sDA): Is a metric used to describe annual sufficiency of ambient daylight in building interiors.

Stakeholder meetings: Meetings that are conducted among the project team, stakeholders, neighbors, and community members in order to understand and discuss community needs, issues, and concerns.

Suburban sprawl: The expansion of populations away from central urban areas into low-density areas.

Systems thinking: Refers to the understanding of each and every system of a building while also understanding their relationships and looking at the project as a whole.

Vision glazing: The term used for windows that provide exterior views.

Water balance approach: Aims to balance the water supply with water consumption.

Wet pond (retention pond): Pond designed to hold a specific amount of water indefinitely.

Xeriscaping: Type of landscaping that does not need any irrigation.

Zero-lot project: A type of project which the building footprint covers the whole lot.